THE WASHERDRIER & TUMBLEDRIER MANUAL

DIY Plumbing □ Maintenance □ Repair

Graham Dixon

Haynes

© Graham Dixon 1993

Published by:
Haynes Publishing Group
Sparkford, Nr Yeovil, Somerset
BA22 7JJ, England

Haynes Publishing Inc.
861 Lawrence Drive,
Newbury Park,
California 91320 USA

British Library Cataloguing in Publication Data

A catalogue record for this book is available from the British Library

ISBN 1 85010 892 7 (Book Trade)

ISBN 1 85010 893 5 (Motor Trade)

Printed in Great Britain by
J. H. Haynes & Co. Ltd.

Contents

Acknowledgements 4

Chapter 1
Introduction 5

Chapter 2
Emergency procedures 10

Chapter 3
Tools and equipment 11

Chapter 4
A general safety guide 12

Chapter 5
Using a flowchart 14

Chapter 6
Basics – Electrical 16

Chapter 7
Plugs and sockets 19

Chapter 8
Basics – Plumbing 28

Chapter 9
Venting 31

Chapter 10
Functional testing 33

Chapter 11
Locating a fault 35

Chapter 12
General care and attention 36

Chapter 13
Determining the fault 38

Chapter 14
Leaks – Fault finding 42

Chapter 15
Machine will not empty 46

Chapter 16
Door seal fitting 48

Chapter 17
Water inlet valves 56

Chapter 18
Water level control 61

Chapter 19
Pumps 68

Chapter 20
Door switches (interlocks) 74

Chapter 21
Heaters 79

Chapter 22
Temperature control 85

Chapter 23
Drying components and
faults (washerdriers) 93

Chapter 24
Timers (programmers) 101

Chapter 25
Suspension 113

Chapter 26
Low insulation 118

Chapter 27
Motors 125

Chapter 28
Belts 141

Chapter 29
Suppressors 145

Chapter 30
Bearings 147

Chapter 31
Using a meter 163

Chapter 32
Wiring and harness faults 167

Chapter 33
Dry-only machines 169

Chapter 34
Useful tips and
information 181

Chapter 35
Buying spare parts 183

Chapter 36
Know your machine 185

Chapter 37
Common causes of poor
washing results 187

Chapter 38
Successful stain removal 189

Chapter 39
Care labelling in the UK 194

Chapter 40
Jargon 199

Acknowledgements

The author would like to extend his thanks and gratitude to the following people and organisations for their help in the compilation of certain sections of this book.

Oracstar Ltd.
Lever Bros.
Crabtree Electrical Industries Ltd.

Thanks also to Andrew Morland for much of the photographic work and Martin Coltman for some of the illustrations.

Chapter 1

Introduction

Today's modern automatic washing machines/tumbledriers are the highly refined offspring of their predecessors. Many refinements have been made to aid production and to cut production costs for the manufacturer, although it is fair to say that improvements to washing and spin speeds have also been incorporated. The automatic washing machine has changed little in its basic operation over the years apart from the obvious cosmetic changes and additions of faster spin speeds and increased wash variations. In recent years the washing machine and tumbledrier have been combined in the washerdrier. These changes have not significantly increased the overall cost of automatic machines and in real terms, they are actually cheaper now than twenty five years ago. With the use of electronics to control motor speeds and the high demand for machines, mass production techniques and a competitive market have kept costs relatively low.

The main drawback has been in the cost of repairs and servicing your appliance once the guarantee has expired. Many people have opted for the five year cover offered by manufacturers only to find that in some cases only the defective part is covered and not the wear and tear, and in particular, not the labour charge for fitting the replacement part.

This often results in a small repair, e.g. replacement of a belt, still costing around £45. The breakdown of which is the cost of the belt approximately £5 is waived, but the call-out and repair charge of £40 or more plus VAT is levied.

This book looks at the combined automatic washerdrier and separate tumbledry only machines in detail. The aim of the book is to help you to understand these machines and to show that they are not as complex as one may at first sight imagine. In fact, the majority of all repairs are within the scope of most owners. With a little thought, planning and understanding of how your machine and its components operate, you will not only be able to save money but also gain the satisfaction of completing a repair yourself often without the delay encountered when contacting a repair company. Even if you are on a five year cover, repair it yourself when parts are less than labour charge and pass on to the manufacturer the jobs needing expensive parts. This action may invalidate subsequent claims in some instances.

This book has been written for those who possess little or no practical knowledge of washing machines or their faults. Seasoned DIY car mechanics will find the book useful as many of the problems

found with the washing machine are similar to those on cars e.g. worn or noisy bearings, faulty hoses, suspension, etc.

Approached in a logical step-by-step manner, not as a haphazard guess, most if not all faults are within the capabilities of the DIY person. The book is best read cover to cover to gain the gist of flowchart use and to familiarise yourself with procedures and the best ways to locate and rectify faults that may occur. You can then use the book as a quick reference guide before and during repairs. It is impossible to deal specifically with any particular machine as models vary considerably with each manufacturer having their own style of pumps, hoses, bearing sizes, etc., but the concept of an automatic washer, washerdrier or tumbledrier differs very little between manufacturers. This will become apparent after reading through the book.

Having read the book, you will become more aware of safety around the home due to a better understanding of electrical items and their limitations. Regular checks for faults which can be rectified prior to failure or accident greatly increase the safety of your appliances. You will gain more efficient use of your items through understanding their correct operation.

The machines in the photo sequences have been selected as a cross section of some of the most popular ones found in homes today. Both old and new machines are used in the sequences to highlight actual fault areas and faults to look out for. All names and model numbers are used for customer reference purposes only. At all times, before working on a machine, make sure that it is isolated from both the electrical supply, i.e. switch off socket and remove plug, and from the water supply by turning off the feed taps. This ensures your safety and that of the machine and its surroundings.

This book has been split into two separate sections: first, the washerdrier, both vented and condenser types, (this section covers all aspects of the machine including parts of the drier) and secondly, the separate drier only machines in detail. N.B. The sections on Basics, Safety, motors and timers, etc., are common to both versions therefore it is essential to read the whole book.

THE WASHERDRIER

There are two main types of automatic washerdriers:
(a) Those that allow the warm moisture laden air to escape through a vent usually positioned at the rear of the machine, easily spotted by its large diameter. This type of machine requires a vent hose to the outside, either through an open window or through the wall vent system (explained later in the book). The machine can be used without venting but will result in moisture laden air discharged by the machine on a drying cycle condensing on cold surfaces in the same room (i.e. windows, cupboards, walls, etc.). For the machine to be used economically, and in order to avoid problems with damp cupboards, etc., it is advisable to vent the machine in some way.
(b) Condenser washerdriers use the same system of rotating the wash load in a stream of warm air following the final spin but do not vent the resulting moisture laden air out of the machine. The warm moist air is allowed to pass over an internal condenser unit within the machine. This unit is kept cool by passing a small amount of cold water through it via an extra cold water inlet valve, and when the warm air meets this cold surface the moisture is condensed from it. The resulting liquid is allowed to collect at

the bottom of the outer tub ready to be discharged by the outlet pump through the drain hose of the machine. The warm air with the moisture removed is then recycled via the drier heater making this style of machine more economical than the straight vent to atmosphere machines described in A. The condenser washerdrier requires no extra fittings than is needed for a normal automatic washing machine.

The repair and maintenance of automatic washerdriers is similar to ordinary automatic washing machines and many parts such as valves, pumps, pressure switches, etc., may be common to other machines within the manufacturers' range of both wash only and combined washerdriers. The main differences are the addition of fan and heater to supply warm air, larger vents on outer tub, door seals with hot air intake aperture and timers with dry cycle position. Some machines will also have separate timers for the drying cycle; more of these in the Timer chapter. Another difference is the restricted space within the machine in which to carry out repairs. This is due to the added bulk of the fan and heater assembly as well as the external condenser unit on condenser machines.

COMBINED WASHERDRIERS IN MORE DETAIL

As mentioned earlier, washerdriers fall into two categories:
(1) Vented – those that simply expel the moisture laden air (usually from a vent at the rear of the machine).
(2) Condenser – the use of a recirculating airflow with a system for removing the moisture form the airflow by condensing it back to water within the machine. As can be

seen from the following text and drawings, both versions have many parts in common and although the size and shape of the parts may change, depending on manufacturer, the basic principles are the same. Washerdrier machines, as the name implies, are a combination of an automatic washing machine and a tumbledrier in one machine. As with any combination, compromises have to be made in order to run smoothly and the load size and drying time will not suit every situation.

Combining the auto washer with the tumbledrier is beneficial for the manufacturer. The automatic washing machine already has a drum for the load, a means of rotating it (clockwise and anti-clockwise) and an outlet pump to discharge the water produced by the condenser machines. In simple terms, all that is needed in addition to turn it into a drier would be a fan to circulate air, a heater to warm the air, a means of ducting the air through the drum and a means of timing the length of the dry cycle. Condenser machines would require the addition of an extra cold water valve, plus a condenser unit which could be a simple trickle bar within the wash tub or externally mounted on the outer of the wash tub or inner of the cabinet of the machine. See diagrams.

Faults, repair and maintenance of the machine must be considered as a whole. Many faults will interrelate between the washing sequence of the machine and the drying action, therefore a simple division between the two operations is not always possible. An understanding of all the parts is essential, their correct operation, the way in which they function, the interrelating between them, associated faults and potential areas for trouble. To this end, each item is examined individually and how it relates to

Simple vented type combined washerdrier. This cut away drawing illustrates the basic components of a vented washerdrier and highlights how few extra parts are required over and above a wash only machine. The fan unit, duct and heaters make up part of the top tub weight (A). Cold air is drawn in from the interior shell space of the machine (B) by fan (C). The air drawn in is blown over the heating elements (D) and in doing so, lifts flap (E). Access to the inner drum is by an extra flange/inlet to the door gasket/seal (F). The now warm air picks up moisture from the wash load on its way through the contra rotating drum. The now moisture laden air escapes through the contra rotating drum. Thermostat (G) monitors the air temperature within the outer tub. The now moisture laden air escapes through the vent positioned on the rear of the outer tub unit. A convoluted hose (H) guides the warm moist air to the exterior of the machine. **Note**: A filter is normally situated on the outlet hose to the rear of the machine.

Shown are the basic components and operation of a typical condenser combined washerdrier:
A. Heater duct.
B. Heating element (maybe two).
C. Circulation fan motor.
D. Air circulation fan.
E. Condenser unit externally mounted in this instance on the back of the outer tub.
F. Cold water inlet to spray bar or trickle plate.
G. Normal sump hose to pump.

HOT AIR

DRY WARM AIR

MOISTURE LADEN AIR

WATER AND CONDENSATE

Airflow of front vented tumble dry only machine.
A. Drum.
B. Heater.
C. Fan
D. Cold air inlet.
E. Warm moist air vented through door grille and filter.

other working parts is described in detail. This will help in building up an overall picture of how the machine works, the details of each section and ultimately the interaction of all components during a wash and dry cycle. Where possible, specific faults are given with help regarding checks/action to be carried out.

DRY ONLY MACHINES

The tumbledrier has been with us for many years now. The basic function is to circulate warm air through the damp clothes for a given period of time selected by the user, followed with a cool tumble prior to switching off at the selected time. This is a relatively simple operation requiring a drum to hold the load, a heater

to warm the air and a fan to circulate the warm air through the drum. As with the washing machine, the drum is rotated to allow all the load to gain maximum benefit from the warm air flow. In most instances the motor that revolves the drum also drives the fan used for air circulation. Being a dedicated machine (drying only) it works much more efficiently than its combined washerdrier counterpart. These are several reasons for this. The drum capacity can be much larger as it is not necessary to have a water-tight outer tub thus allowing for a larger drum taking up nearly all the available space within the cabinet. The larger machines (those with cabinets the same size as a washing machine) can take the same size load, i.e. and 11 lb (5 kg) wash load can be transferred directly

into the 11 lb load tumbledrier. The smaller models with a 6 lb (2.7 kg) load capacity, convenient if space is restricted, operates in exactly the same way as the larger models.

The larger drum allows for better movement of the clothing through the airflow, ensuring more even and quicker drying even as the clothing increase in bulk during the drying process. This increases in bulk/size of load is why the washerdrier can dry only half its wash load. A larger wattage heater can be used (if necessary) with a greater surface area for warming the air.

Again, owing to the increase in usable space, a larger fan can be used for circulating the air.

Over the years, additions to the basic principles have been made. Drum rotation on early and current basic machines is in one direction only. Nowadays, the option is to have reverse drum action similar to the wash action (clockwise and counter clockwise). This obviously requires a more complex motor which is capable of rotation in both directions, and a more complex timer or motor reversal system. Temperature control, again on early and current basic models is relatively straightforward with selections of high or low, but on the more recent and expensive machines, auto sensing is now a feature. This system senses the moisture content of the load being dried and switches off when a pre-selected degree of dryness had been reached. The advantage of auto sensing is that it switches off when dry unlike the more basic machine that carries on tumbling and heating for the set time regardless of whether the clothes are dry or not.

Further refinements and extras include computer control (electronic in place of mechanical), intermittent tumble after the drying process is complete which prevents the load compacting at the end of the cycle if left unattended for any length of time prior to removal. Condenser tumbledriers are also available. These operate in a similar manner to the combined washerdrier system by condensing the moisture rather than venting it. Some require water supply and outlet whilst others use cold air instead of water to aid condensing, and a removable container to catch the condensate. The container requires regular emptying (once every two dry cycles on average if not permanently drained in a similar way to the automatic washer, i.e. pump and outlet).

The tumbledriers covered in this book heat the air used in the drying process by electricity, but domestic tumbledriers are now available which heat by gas. Although commercial machines have had this option for several years, it is new to the domestic user. Because of the stringent gas regulations and the obvious need for safety, do not attempt installation or any inspection or repair on this type of product. The installation and repair of gas machines must by done by those with the correct knowledge, equipment and gas qualifications.

The main benefits of the larger dry only machines (same sized cabinet as the washing machine), are that 'it will dry a full wash load, and it can also be drying one load whilst another load is being washed, thus saving a lot of time. **Note:** do not use both machines from a single socket via an adaptor. See Basics (electrical). The separate drier is also quicker and more efficient than washerdriers if used correctly.

DRAWBACKS

For households with restricted space, finding room for another appliance the size of a washing machine can be a problem. **Note:** Some of the smaller machines can stand on work surfaces if necessary and some of the larger models can stack on top of a washing machine, (these usually need to be of the same make and require a stacking frame for safety). Some of the smaller machines can be wall mounted by using a suitable bracket obtainable from the manufacturer. **Note:** See also the chapter on venting.

Chapter 2

Emergency procedures

COMBINED WASHERDRIER MACHINES

With symptoms such as leaking, flooding, unusual noises, blowing fuses, etc., the following procedure should be carried out. It is essential that the machine is NOT allowed to continue its programme until the fault has been located and rectified.

Firstly – Do not panic
(a) Isolate the machine from the mains supply, i.e. turn the machine off, switch off at the wall socket, and remove the plug from the socket.
(b) Turn off the hot and cold taps to which the fill hoses of the machine are connected. This is done because, even with the power turned off, if a valve is at fault it could be jammed in the open position. The machine will still fill, as turning the power or the machine off will make no difference to this type of fault.
(c) At this point, the power and water should be disconnected. Even now, if there is still water in the machine, it could be leaking. Any remaining water can be extracted from the machine by syphoning which is done simply by lifting the outlet hose from its usual position and lowering it to below the level of water in the machine. This will allow water to drain (unless of course, there is a blockage in

the outlet hose!) To stop the water, lift the hose above the height of the machine. Repeat this process until the machine is empty.
(d) Do not open the door to remove the clothes until all the previous steps have been carried out and a few minutes have elapsed to allow the load in the machine to cool. In cases where the machine was on a very hot wash wait about half an hour. When all of these steps have been carried out, and the clothes have been removed from the drum, it is then possible to calmly sit down and start to work out what the problem may be, and form the plan of action in a logical manner.

B.

DRAIN

C.

OUT

A.

D.

Chapter 3

Tools and equipment

Modern automatic washing machines do not require very specialised tools. Many of the routine repairs such as blocked pumps, renewal of door seals and hoses can normally be completed with a selection of the following tools: crossblade and flatblade screwdrivers, combination pliers, simple multimeter, pliers.

Most people who are D.I.Y. orientated will own one or more of these items already. A useful addition to this selection would be a 'Mole' wrench, a socket and/or box spanner set, soft-face hammer and circlip pliers. These would help with the larger jobs, such as motor removal and bearing removal, etc.

Bearing removal/renewal for instance may also require specific equipment such as bearing pullers. As these can be expensive to buy, it is best to hire them from a tool hire specialist for the short period that you require them. Local garages may also be willing to let you hire them for a small deposit.

It will not prove difficult to build up a selection of tools capable of tackling the faults that you are likely to find on your machine. Most of the large D.I.Y. stores will stock the tools that you require, often at a good saving.

When buying tools check the quality. A cheap spanner or socket set is a waste of money if it bends or snaps after only a short period of use. Having said that, there are many tools on the market that are of a reasonable quality and are inexpensive. Try to buy the best that your budget will allow. Remember, the tools that you buy are a long-term investment and should give years of useful service.

As with any investment, it is wise to look after it and tools should be treated in the same way. Having spent time and money on tools, they should be kept in a clean and serviceable condition. Ensure that they are clean and dry before storage.

Chapter 4

A general safety guide

Most people have a healthy respect for electricity and understand its potential of not only being an asset in the way it can be put to so many uses, but in the way it can be a dangerous and sometimes lethal adversary if taken for granted or misused.

Electricity at all voltages is to be respected. Those that do not observe the basic rules of electricity are not only a danger to themselves but to those around them.

Electrical accidents should be regarded as avoidable. Most are due to plain carelessness and the failure to follow basic rules of electricity even when they are known by the injured party.

There are in the region of sixteen million homes in Britain supplied with electricity, each home having on average twenty five electrical appliances. With such a volume of items, it may be a surprise to find that fatalities due to electrical accidents are less than eighty per year. Although this is a small percentage figure in terms of population and only 1% of 8000 deaths resulting from accidents in the home, it is still too high.

The most common causes of shocks or fires from electrical appliances fall into three categories;
1. Faulty wiring of the appliances. i.e. frayed or damaged flex or cables, incorrect fuse, poor socket, poor/damaged plug, incorrectly wired plug, etc.
2. Misuse of the appliance. Hairdriers and similar electrical items being used in the bathroom. This also includes the installation of washing machines, etc., incorrectly installed in bathrooms. Electrical power tools used outside in the rain or in wet conditions. Rules regarding electrical items in bathrooms are strict for good reason. See *Do's and Dont's*. The combination of water and electricity greatly increases the possibility of you or someone else being injured.
3. Continuing to use an electrical appliance knowing it to be unsafe, i.e. cracked casing, faulty plug, damaged cable, faulty on/off switch, etc.

With awareness of the need for safety, several of the above faults are avoidable. Others can be eliminated by regular inspection and immediate correction of faults, failure or wear. As for misuse, this may be due to a purely foolhardy approach or genuine ignorance of potential danger. This can be overcome by understanding and above all, action upon the guidelines in this book. If at anytime you feel you lack the ability to do a particular job yourself, then it is best not to try. You can still carry out the diagnosis of the problem thus ensuring that any work carried out by a repair company is correct. This alone can sometimes save a lot of time and expense.

DO'S

Thoroughly read all the information in this book prior to putting it into practice. Isolate any appliance before repair and/or inspection commences. Make sure that the correct rated fuse is used. Correctly fit the mains plug (See: Basics – Electrical), ensuring the connections are in the correct position, tight and the cord clamp fitted on the outer of the cable. Check that the socket used is in good condition and has a sound earth path. See: Basics – Electrical. Take time to consider the problem at hand and allow enough time to complete the job without rushing. Keep a methodical approach to the stripdown of the item and make notes. This helps greatly with subsequent re-assembly. Double check everything. Ask or seek help if in doubt. Ensure an RCD, see Jargon, is in circuit when functionally testing a machine, and when using electrical equipment outdoors.

DON'TS

Do not work on any machine that is still plugged in even if the socket switch is **'OFF'**. Always isolate fully – **PLUG OUT**. Do not install or allow the use of washing machines, tumbledriers or any portable mains appliance in bathrooms or shower rooms. It may seem harmless to run an extension lead from a convenient socket on the landing so that an appliance can be used in the bathroom, but it is extremely dangerous and **MUST NOT** be done under any circumstances. Do not use mains powered equipment outdoors in damp conditions or outdoors in the rain. Do not repair damaged wiring or cables with insulation tape under any circumstances. Do not sacrifice safety by effecting a temporary repair.

Switch off! Always withdraw plug and disconnect from mains.

Appliances vary – make sure you have a suitable replacement part.

For screws use a screwdriver, for nuts a spanner.

Examine and clean all connections before fitting new parts.

Tighten firmly all screws and nuts (knurled nuts, use pliers).

Your safety depends on these simple rules.

Fuses: Up to 250 watts 1 amp; 750 watts 3 amp; 750 to 3000 watts 13 amp.

Insulation is for your protection. Don't interfere.

Renew worn or damaged appliance flex.

Secure flex clamps and all protective covers.

Test physically and electrically on completion.

WARNING: Never leave bare wires outside terminals.

Note: The wires in a mains lead are coloured in accordance with the following code: Green and Yellow – Earth, Blue – Neutral, Brown – Live. As the colours of the wires in the mains lead of an appliance may not correspond with the coloured markings identifying the terminals in the plug, proceed as follows. The wire which is coloured green and yellow must be connected to the terminal which is marked with the letter 'E' or by the earth symbol or coloured green or green and yellow. The wire which is coloured blue must be connected to the terminal which is marked with the letter 'N' or coloured black. The wire which is coloured brown must be connected to the terminal which is marked with the letter 'L' or coloured red. If in doubt, consult a qualified electrician.

The correct rating of fuse must be used as per the manufacturer's instructions.

Consider your own safety and that of other people.

Act in a way that prevents incidents becoming accidents.

Use your common sense........think before acting.

Tidy workplaces make safer workplaces.

Identify potential hazards.

Observe the rule of safety first.

Never underestimate the possible dangers.

The author would like to point out at this time, that any references to manufacturer's names or model numbers, etc., that are used throughout this manual are for the reader's information, and reference purposes only. Whilst every precaution has been taken to ensure that all information is factual in every detail, the author cannot accept any responsibility for any errors or omissions appertaining to this manual.

Chapter 5

Using a flowchart

Flowcharts are used throughout the book, and are designed to help you quickly locate the area or areas of trouble, and to show that a step-by-step approach to even the most difficult of faults, is by far the best way to ensure they are found and rectified easily. The use of flowcharts, to those with some experience of home computers, will need little explanation. To those of you that will be seeing them for the first time, here is how they work.

HOW FLOWCHARTS WORK

To the uninitiated, the use of flowcharts may seem a difficult way of fault finding. This is not the case, and will be quite simple if a few small, but important points are remembered. As you will see in the examples, there are only three main types of symbols used. A rectangular box, a diamond and an ellipse. With a little practise, you will become aware how invaluable this method can be in all areas of D.I.Y. work. The construction of one's own flowchart before attempting the job in hand, will be of help when the time comes to reverse the stripdown procedure, i.e. notes can be made next to the relevant boxes on the flowchart, of what was encountered at that point, e.g. number of screws, positions of

wires, etc., small points, but vital, and so often forgotten with an unplanned approach.

THE RECTANGULAR BOX

This is a process, i.e. in the box is an instruction. Carry it out, and rejoin the flowchart where you left it, travelling in the direction indicated by the arrows.

THE ELLIPSE

This is a terminator. When this box is encountered, you either start a new chart or finish one. The text in the box will indicate the action.

THE DIAMOND

This asks a question, i.e. if the answer to the question in the diamond is 'yes', then follow the line from the point of the box, e.g. the box asks if a pipe is blocked. The junction to the left is marked 'no', and the junction to the right is marked 'yes'. If the pipe is blocked, follow the line to the right.

The following example illustrates the steps involved in carrying out the simple task of opening a closed door, and closing an open door. The arrows indicate the direction to the next step, so as to guide you through the logical sequence.

The following example flowchart illustrates the steps involved in carrying out the simple task of opening a closed door, and closing an open door. The arrows indicate the direction to the next step, so as to guide you through the logical sequence.

Chapter 6

Basics – Electrical

For the sake of safety around the home or office, a basic understanding of electricity is essential. Even if you don't intend to carry out any repairs or servicing of your appliances yourself, a sound understanding of household electrical supply will prove invaluable in the long run. Ignorance is no protection against either yours or a third party's errors, whether it be on repairs, servicing or the installation of appliances. It is with this in mind that this chapter has been written. It is not an in-depth study of the subject, there are many books that contain more detailed information for those who want to know more about electricity. In this instance, the aim is to impart a safe knowledge without too much technical data. A simplified, but typical household supply is as follows.

The substation has power supplied to it at very high voltage (400,000 volts) in three-phase form. This supply is converted at the substation via a transformer, down to 240 volt single-phase and is then distributed to our homes. Under normal circumstances, current flows from the live supply of the substation's transformer, through the electrical items being used in the house and back via the neutral conductor (cable) to the substation transformer's neutral pole (a closed loop). The neutral terminal of the transformer is in turn connected to the ground (earth – meaning in this case, the general mass of the earth).

It is usual to use the armoured sheath of the electricity supply authority's cable in order to provide a low impedance continuous link back to the supply transformer's start point. Various types of earthing can be encountered; connection to the armoured sheath of the authority's supply cable, own earth rod, transformer earth rod via general mass of the earth or the increasingly popular use of the neutral conductor of the authority's supply cable (often called P.M.E. – protective multiple earthing or TN-C-S system). If with any of the mentioned earth systems a fault should occur between the live conductor and the earth conductor, another loop would be formed. This is called the 'earth loop' for obvious reasons. The earth loop path is designed to encourage current to flow in the event of an earth fault, to enable the protective device in the consumer unit to operate in order to isolate the supply to the circuit. Failure to cause the protective device to operate will result in the appliance remaining 'live' with the consequence that any person touching the appliance will receive a nasty, if not fatal electric shock. For this reason the resistance of the earth loop path must be low enough to allow sufficient fault current to flow to operate the protective fuse or circuit breaker.

It is very important not only to have an earth, but one that has a low resistance/impedance, i.e. perfect earth. The term used for testing for this is earth loop impedance, which means checking to see if the current flow is impeded and if it is, by how much. This test requires a specialised meter giving a resistance figure on ohms, the maximum reading recommended by the I.E.E. being 1.1ohms. **Note:** A correct test cannot be carried out using a low voltage test meter as a fault may exist that allows the low voltage of say 9 volts to pass easily, (i.e. just one tiny strand of wire poorly connected), but would break down and go high resistance or open circuit if a true fault voltage of 240 v at 13 amps tried to be passed.

Though low voltage testing will give an indication of earth path, it cannot indicate quality. Only an earth loop impedance meter gives a clearer indication of earth quality under more realistic conditions.

WHAT IS AN EARTH FAULT?

An earth fault is defined as the condition where electricity flows to earth which, under normal circumstances it should not do. There are two recognised ways in which this may happen – Direct and Indirect.

Direct. This is when contact is made directly with the current-carrying conductor which is designed to carry that current, i.e. possibly as a result of failure to isolate the supply or by ignoring safety precautions, etc.

Indirect. Touching a part or metal casing, etc., that would not normally carry current but is doing so owing to a fault.

Consumer units with both M.C.B.s with R.C.D.s (residual current devices) provide a much higher degree of protection.

WHAT IS A CONSUMER UNIT?

The consumer unit is the point at which the supply into the house is split into separate circuits, i.e. lights, sockets, etc. It houses a main isolation switch or combined R.C.D. which is used to isolate/remove power to all the circuits in the house. Also housed within the unit are various fuse carriers for cartridge or rewireable fuses or an M.C.B. in place of fuses. Each circuit leading from the consumer unit has its own rating of fuse of M.C.B. and only that fuse rating and no other may be used.
Note: Even when switched off, there is still a live supply to the consumer unit. Do not remove the covers of the consumer unit or tackle any inspection or repair to this item without seeking further information. Faults other than fuse renewal are best left to skilled electrical engineers. Although assistance may be available from other publications, extreme care should be exercised. As mentioned earlier, it is not the aim of this book to invite the repair or maintenance of items that are not fully isolated.

WHAT DOES IT DO?

The consumer unit's function is to divide the incoming supply at a convenient point (though not always easily accessible due to poor design). It also allows all circuits to be allocated a fuse and to conveniently house them in one unit. Isolation of all circuits is possible by a main double-pole switch which is also incorporated within the unit.

FUSES IN MORE DETAIL

As mentioned earlier, two versions of fuses are to be found. Cartridge and rewireable fuses have been around for sometime now. The rewireable type being difficult and fiddly and the cartridge type, although easier to renew, is often difficult to obtain. Both these systems have drawbacks in being awkward and not very 'user friendly'.

An ordinary fuse is simply a weak link designed to break/rupture at a preset rating. If a circuit is overloaded or a short circuit occurs, the resulting overload will cause the fuse to melt and sever the supply. Unless a direct short circuit occurs, the overload on the fuse may not be enough to cause the fuse to blow as it has a fair degree or leeway over its rating value. It therefore offers only basic safety and will not afford any personal safety as the time taken to break/rupture is generally too long.

Miniature circuit breakers (M.C.B.) are now widely used which avoid all the problems normally associated with ordinary fuses. They are small sophisticated units that afford a much high degree of protection than the ordinary fuses. They are tamper-proof and are easily identified when one has tripped (switch moves to "off" position). Most importantly, they cannot be reset if the fault still exists which eliminates the practice of putting in the wrong fuse wire or cartridge to get things working – a foolish and most dangerous practice! M.C.B.s are available in similar ratings to ordinary fuses.
These units are factory calibrated to extremely accurate tolerances and must not be tampered with or attempts made to re-adjust.

Unfortunately, neither fuses nor miniature circuit breakers alone can give protection to anyone involved in a 'direct contact' situation and it is quite possible for the same statement to apply in the case of 'indirect contact'. This may sound confusing, but it should be realised that in a 'direct contact' situation a person is literally shorting out Live and Earth whereas in an 'indirect contact' situation, the Live to Earth path is already there because the equipment itself is connected to earth. The reason the fuse hasn't blown or the circuit breaker tripped is because the fault is not large enough to operate them, yet is large enough to be fatal. For instance, a 10 amp fuse would never blow with an 8 amp earth fault on the circuit, yet 8 amps constitutes a very dangerous level of earth fault current.

To afford a higher degree of protection, another device has been developed and is available in various forms.
(a) Mounted within the consumer unit to protect all or selected circuits.
(b) As individual socket protection.
(c) An adaptor to be used as portable protection and used where required.

The name given to this device in all its forms is an R.C.D. (Residual Current Device). It may also be called R.C.C.B. (Residual Current Circuit Breaker). In the early days of its introduction, it was known as an E.L.C.B. (Earth Leakage Circuit Breaker). The primary protection is the integrity of the earthing. RCDs in addition to the earthing, provide a much higher degree of protection depending upon the degree of sensitivity. For personal protection it is recommended that a sensitivity of 30 mA is used.

It is generally considered that an earth fault of 1 amp or more is a fire risk, 50 mA or more provides a shock risk which can have varying effects upon the human body depending upon the value of earth fault current and the body resistance of the person and of course, their state of health. The heartbeat cycle is about 0.75 second. it is therefore necessary to cut off the fault current in less than one cardiac cycle. The Wiring Regulations stipulate that for

Indirect Contact protection isolation must occur within 0.4 second.

HOW DOES AN R.C.D. WORK?

An R.C.D. protects by constantly monitoring the current flowing in the live and neutral wires supplying a circuit or an individual item of equipment. Under normal circumstances, the current flowing in the two wires is equal but, when an earth leakage occurs due to the fault or an accident, an imbalance occurs and this is detected by the R.C.D. which automatically cuts off the power within 200 mS.

To be effective, the R.C.D. must operate very quickly and at a low earth leakage current. Those most frequently recommended are designed to detect earth leakage faults in excess of 30 mA (30/1000ths of an amp) and to disconnect the power supply with 30 ms (30/1000ths of a second); these limits are well inside the safety margin without which electrocution or fire would not be expected to occur.

It should now be apparent that R.C.Ds are designed to sever mains current should your electrical appliance develop an electrical fault or should you cut through the mains cable of your lawnmower for instance. They are not designed to let you increase the risk to yourself by adopting a cavalier attitude with regard to safety. They are simply a fail safe device and should be used as such. Used correctly they are an invaluable asset to your household.

Note: The use of an R.C.D. must be in addition to and not instead of normal overload protective; i.e. fuses of M.C.Bs. All residual current devices have a test button facility. It is essential that this is pressed regularly to verify that the device operates. For use with adaptors or sockets, or for outside use, test before each operation. If failure occurs, i.e. does not trip, or trip appears sluggish or hard to obtain, have the unit tested immediately. This will require an R.C.D. test meter and is best left to a qualified electrician.

Chapter 7

Plugs and sockets

Problems with electrical appliances may not always be the result of a failure of the item itself but with the electrical supply to it via the socket. A three-pin socket must have a 'live' supply, a 'neutral' return and a sound earth path. When a plug from an appliance is inserted in the socket, a firm contact must be made at all three points. If the live or neutral pins of the plug or connection point within the socket fail to make adequate contact or are free to move, localised heating will occur within the socket.

HOW CAN YOU TELL?

Tell-tale signs of this type of fault often show themselves as;
1. Burn marks around one or both entry points on the socket.
2. Plug hot to the touch after use of appliance in that socket.
3. Pungent smell from socket when appliance is in use.
4. Pitting and burn marks on and around the pins of the plug.
5. Radio interference to nearby equipment caused by the internal arcing within the socket creating spurious radio emissions that may also pass along the ring main to hi-fi units, etc.
6. Intermittent or slow operation of the appliance being used.

7. Failure of the fuse in the plug. In this instance, not caused by a fault within the appliance but by heat being transferred through the live pin and into the fuse which fails by over heating.

All the above mentioned are more pronounced with higher current draw appliances such as washing machines, tumbledriers, etc.

WHY DOES IT HAPPEN?

The reason for such problems are varied and may be caused by one or a combination of any of those listed below:
(a) Frequent use of the socket opening up the contact points within the socket (general wear and tear).
(b) Poor quality socket, plug or both.
(c) Loose pins on plug.
(d) The use of a double adaptor. This can cause a poor connection purely by the weight of cables and plugs not allowing a tight fit in the socket, or worse still, allowing two high current draw appliances to be run through one socket thus overloading the single 13 amp socket, e.g. washing machine and tumbledrier.

Whenever possible, avoid the use of adaptors by provision of an adequate number of sockets and do not exceed 3 kW load on the single socket.

(e) Use of multi-point extension lead when the total load on the trailing socket can easily exceed the safe 3 kW load of the single socket.

WHAT CAN BE DONE IF THIS HAPPENS?

Firstly, do not use the socket until the problem has been rectified. If the socket is found to be showing any of the previously described faults, it must be renewed completely. If it is a single socket, it may be wise at this point to have a double socket fitted as a replacement. There are dozens of books that describe the renewal of sockets and the need to duplicate their instructions here is unnecessary as the aim of this book is to cover problems the others do not. Suffice to say that caution and regard to safety must be considered when tackling socket renewal. When buying a replacement socket, make sure it is a good quality one as there are many of dubious quality to be found. Price is a good indicator of quality in this field.

It is advisable at this stage to renew the plugs that have been used in the faulty socket as damage may have been done to the plug. To continue using the old plugs could result in premature failure of your new unit.

Socket highlighting overheating. Both plug and socket will require replacing.

As with sockets, plugs can be found in many styles and qualities. While some of the poorer quality plugs may prove to be reliable on low current consumption items like lamps, TV and radios, they may not be so good for washing machines and tumbledriers, etc. Although British Standards do apply to these items, quality does vary considerably. When buying plugs and sockets, go to outlets that can give advice and that carry a good selection. This will allow you to compare quality and build of the products. Look for the ASTA mark which proves that the design and manufacture has been approved by the Association of Short Circuit Testing Authories. Replacement fuses should also carry this mark.

All of the faults mentioned previously relate to the 'live' supply and neutral return on either the socket, plug or both. There is of course a third pin, although it takes no active part in the operation of the appliance, it is however the most important connection of all. Products that have 3 core cable must have the yellow and green earth wire securely connected to the earth pin of the plug or pin market E.

Wiring Guide-inside view

Green or
Green-Yellow

Black or Blue

E

N

FUSE

L

Red or Brown

Cord Grip

Press cord between Grip before
connecting Conductors to Terminals

TRIM 3 CORES
SAME LENGTH

8 mm 5/16

38 mm 1 1/2

16540 ED1

**APPROVED BY
ASTA
REF AR1**

MK

**FITTED WITH
13 AMP FUSE**

Specific requirements for MK plugs.

checking the socket for reverse polarity. Simply speaking, indicating whether a socket has been incorrectly wired as these sockets can still work and outwardly give no sign of any problem. This type of fault is dangerous and not uncommon. The plug-in tester also indicates if an earth path is present, or not. However the quality of the earth in the socket is not shown. That is to say that it may have a very high resistance but would still allow the neon of the tester to light. If the earth resistance is high, remember this may result in a failure to blow the fuse which may cause overheating at the high resistance point or allow a flow of electricity through anything or anyone else that can give a better route to earth. All household wiring must conform to I.E.E. recommendations. The requirements for the earth path is that it has as low a resistance as possible. Current regulations allow a maximum of 1.1 ohms. This can only be checked fully with an earth loop test meter.

HOW CAN THE EARTH PATH BE CHECKED?

The earth path of an appliance can be checked easily using a simple test meter (see – Using a meter). Remember, a path of low resistance is required from all items within the product that are linked into the earth path via the yellow and green cable.
Note: The maximum reading of 1 ohm. from any point to the earth pin is recommended.

Checking the socket will require the use of an earth loop test meter which needs to be operated correctly. As these

meters are expensive and problems could be encountered with distribution boards fitted with an RCCD (See: What is an RCCD?), it is advisable to have these tests done by a qualified electrical contractor. The simple plug-in testers like the one shown, can be found in most good electrical shop and D.I.Y. outlets. This is most useful for

Internal view of severe burnout caused by poor connection to terminal. A new plug is required and the cable cut back to sound wire or renewed.

High quality three-pin plug ideal for home appliances.

Typical plug-in socket tester.

Typical moulded plug.

Incorrectly fitted plug. Wiring bunched and not trimmed to right lengths. Ensure all plugs are fitted correctly.

Make sure a moulded plug removed from an appliance cannot be inadvertently plugged in. Remove the fuse and bend the pins.

Typical resilient plugs which can stand up to rugged use without cracking.

Wiring not cut to correct length. As a result the cord grip is fixed across inner wires not outer sheath.

Conductor wire protruding from plug pins.

Wiring incorrectly bunched into plug to allow cord grip to hold outer sheath.

Note: All of the above photographs are used to illustrate the lack of attention to safety to this small but vital component. Always fit plugs correctly and safely. To give further assistance, a step-by-step photo guide for the two types of plug is given overleaf.

WIRING A PLUG

Many people think the fitting of a plug is a straightforward task that needs little or no explanation. On the contrary, this is an area where many problems are to be found and dangers encountered if the fitting is not done correctly. Do not neglect this most important item.

The following text and photo sequences deal specifically with modern 13 amp flat pin plugs. If your property has round pin plugs and sockets, the indication is that the house wiring may be old and it would be advisable to have it checked thoroughly.

When wiring a plug, it is advisable to leave the earth wire (yellow/green) longer than the live and neutral wires, the extra length being formed into a slight sloop shape within the plug. Fixing in this way allows the earth cable to be the last one to pull out should the cable be pulled or caught. If the cord grip is unable to hold the cable in position, the inner wires would tear free from their fixing points. However, the post and nut plug shown does not allow for this to be done and the manufacturer recommends that all wires be cut to the same length.

WIRING A PLUG – PILLAR TYPE

1. Remove the screw that holds the plug top/cover in position, taking care not to lose it.

2. Ease the fuse from position (if using a screwdriver, take care not to damage it).

3. Check that the fuse supplied with the plug is of the correct rating for the appliance. Many plugs are supplied with 13 amp fuse already fitted, but do not be tempted to use it unless it is right. In this instance a 3 amp fuse was required.

5. Offer the wiring to the plug base with the outer sheath in its correct position resting in the cord clamp area. Next, cut the inner cables to suit, allowing ½ in (13mm) past the fixing point. Don't forget to allow a little extra on the earth cable to form a slight loop.

6. Carefully remove ¼ in (6mm) of insulation from the end of each wire. This must be done with care to avoid damaging or cutting any strands of the conductor.

4. Carefully remove the outer cable sheath to expose the inner wires. If damage should occur to the inner wires in the process, cut back and start again.

7. Twist the strands of each wire securely together. Make sure there are no loose strands.

8. Fit each wire into its correct pillar and tighten each screw ensuring that it grips the conductor firmly (with thin wires it will help if they are folded over on themselves first). Make sure the wire fits up to the insulation shoulder and no wires or strands protrude from the pillar.

9 Fit the cord clamp over the outer sheath and screw it firmly into position while being careful not to strip the threads of the plastic grip.

10. Before refitting the top/cover, double check all fixings. Ensure the wiring is seated and routed neatly and is not under stress or bunched. Fit the correct rated fuse, making sure that it is firmly and securely positioned.

11. With top/cover refitted tighten the securing screw.

WIRING A PLUG – POST AND NUT TYPE

1. Remove the screw that holds plug top/cover in position.

2. Remove the knurled/slotted nuts and place them safely in the top.

3. With the plug top/cover removed, the fuse can be eased from its position. If using a screwdriver, take care not to damage the fuse.

6. Now remove $\frac{9}{16}$ in (15 mm) of insulation from the end of each wire. This must be done with care to avoid damaging or cutting any strands of the conductor.

8. The prepared cable can now be inserted into the cord grip ensuring only the outer sheath of the cable is gripped.

4. Check that the fuse supplied with the plug is of the correct rating for the appliance. Many plugs are supplied with 13 amp fuse already fitted but do not be tempted to use it unless it is right. In this instance a 13 amp fuse was required.

7. Twist the strands of each wire securely together. Make sure there are no loose strands.

9. Fit each conductor (wire) to its correct terminal. Make sure each is fitted in a clockwise direction otherwise it will be pushed out as the nut is tightened. Ensure only the conductor is gripped and not the outer insulation.

5. Carefully remove $1\frac{1}{4}$ in (32 mm) of the cable sheath to expose the inner wires. If damage should occur to the inner wires in the process, cut back and start again.

10. Securely tighten all three nuts. Ensure that the wire fits up to the insulation shoulder and no wires or strands protrude from the terminal. Before refitting the top/cover, double-check all fixings. Ensure the wiring is seated and routed neatly and is not under stress or bunched. Fit the correct rated fuse, making sure that it is firmly and securely positioned.

11. *With top/cover refitted tighten the securing screw. This type has a captive screw with a shockproof washer to prevent it working loose during use.*

MOULDED PLUGS

Some appliances may be supplied with moulded 13 amp plugs fitted to the mains cable. If for any reason this plug has to be removed, e.g. for allowing the cable to be slotted through a hole in a work surface, or due to damage, etc., because of its moulded construction, it is not possible to take off in the normal way. The plug has to be cut off with suitable wire cutters and a new plug fitted correctly as shown. **Please note.** Any moulded plug removed in this way must be disposed of immediately. It is wise to remove the fuse and to bend the pins of the plug as soon as it is removed to make sure that it cannot be inadvertently plugged into a socket. Do not leave it lying about and dispose of it where children or the unwary cannot find it and unwittingly plug it in.

DO'S and DON'TS

DO ensure the cable insulation is removed carefully. The use of correct wire strippers is recommended.

DO make sure that connections are the right way around.
See diagrams.

DO ensure that wires are trimmed to suit plug fixing points and no bunching is present.

DO make sure that all connections are tight and no strands of wire are left protruding from terminals. To avoid this, twist strands together as shown prior to fitting.

DO make sure that cord grip is fitted correctly around the outer insulation only.

DO ensure correct rating of fuse is used to suit appliance.

DO ensure the plug top/cover fits tightly and securely with no cracks or damage present.

DO NOT damage the inner core of wires when removing the outer or inner insulation. If you do, cut back and start again.

DO NOT fit tinned ends of cables into plugs. Some manufacturers tin (dip in solder) the end of the exposed inner conductors and also expose the inner wires by removal of the outer insulation. Do not be tempted to fit a plug straight on to such a cable, leaving the inner wires to be gripped by the cord clamp. There are two important reasons why this should not be done;
1. The tinned/soldered end, if fitted to the plug, will work loose and cause problems associated with loose connections. This is due to the solder slowly shrinking from the pressure of the fixing point. Although tight when fitted, the constant pressure over a long period will compress the soft solder resulting in a loose joint.
2. The excessive length of exposed inner wire may protrude below the cord clamp fixing point or force the cable to bunch within the plug to allow the cord clamp to clamp the outer insulation only. Both of these practices are dangerous and must be avoided. Always cut cable lengths to suit the plug to which it is to be attached. If this poor method of fitting is found on an appliance it must be corrected immediately. DO NOT allow strands of wire to protrude from any fixing points. DO NOT fit incorrect fuse ratings. Always match fuses to appliances and observe manufacturer's instructions. DO NOT re-use overheated or damaged plugs. DO NOT bypass the internal fuse.

PLUGS
AND SOCKETS
FLOWCHART

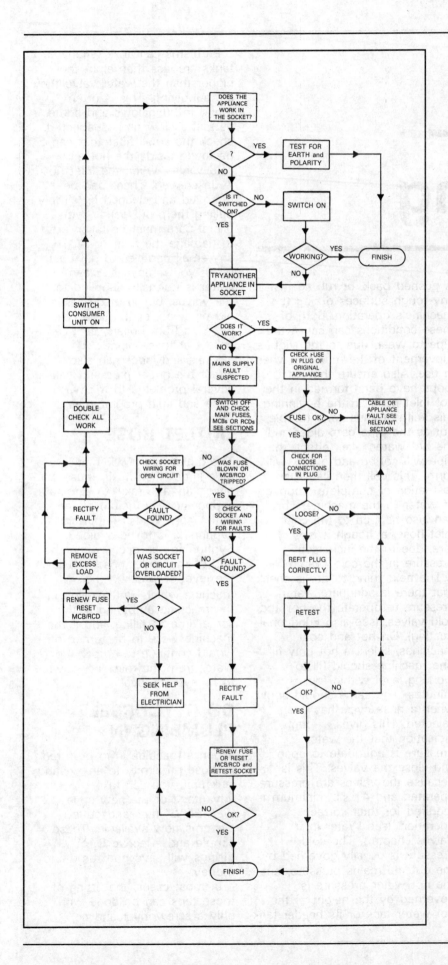

Chapter 8

Basics – Plumbing

Although the machine may have been working correctly in its present position for some time, incorrect installation of a machine may cause faults many months later. Because of this time span, the faults are not associated with bad plumbing and can cause the D.I.Y. engineer to look for other faults, which is very time consuming and annoying. Having said this, it is therefore worth a few minutes examining pipework, and checking the manufacturer's installation details. These details will be found in the manufacturer's booklet that came with the machine. Even if the installation of your machine was left to an 'expert', it is still advisable to read this section, as the chances are that they will not have read the installation details either!

For those of you who cannot find the manufacturer's booklet, what follows is a brief description of plumbing requirements that apply to nearly all automatic washing machines, and the reasons that they should be observed.

If the machine is to be plumbed in 'Hot and Cold', then isolation taps must be fitted. This enables the water supply to be cut off (isolated) between the normal house supply and that of the washer. **Note**: The rubber hoses connected to the isolation taps should be positioned so that they don't get trapped when the machine

is pushed back, or rub against any rough surfaces during the machine's operation. Both of these conditions can cause the pipe to wear, due to the slight movement of the machine when in use. Also ensure that no loops have been formed in the hot inlet hose. In the beginning this will not cause any trouble, but as the pipe gets older and the hot water takes effect, the pipe will soften and a kink will form. This will then cause a restriction or complete stoppage of water to the machine. This can also happen to the cold inlet hose, although it is very rare, due to the increased pressure in the cold system.

The next thing to do, is check that there is adequate water pressure to operate the hot and cold valves, (see also Functional Testing). On hot and cold machines, select a hot only fill. The machine should fill to working level within four minutes. The same should apply when a rinse cycle has been selected. This gives a rough indication that the water pressure is adequate to open and close the valves. This is because the valves are pressure operated and 4 p.s.i. minimum is required for their correct operation, (see Water Inlet Valves chapter). The cold pressure is usually governed by the outside mains pressure, but the hot water pressure is governed by the height of the hot water tank or its header tank.

Problems can arise when the tanks are less than eight feet higher than the water valve they are supplying. This is often found in bungalows and some flats. If a slow fill is suspected, check the small filter that can be found inside the hot and cold valves, when the inlet hose is unscrewed. These can be removed and cleaned by simply pulling them out gently with pliers. Care must be taken not to damage the filter or allow any small particles to get past when you remove it. Clean water is normally supplied to the valves, but in many cases old pipework or the limescale deposits from boilers, etc., can collect at these points.

Kinks and loops can also affect the outlet pipe and cause several problems to the wash, rinse and spin programmes.

OUTLET HOSE

The outlet hose MUST fit into a pipe larger than itself, thus giving an 'air brake' to eliminate syphoning. The height of the outlet hose is also important if syphoning is to be avoided. Syphoning can occur when the end of the outlet hose is below the level of water in the machine which would result in the machine emptying at the same time as filling, and if the machine were to be turned off, would continue to empty the water from the machine, down to its syphon level.

DO IT YOURSELF PLUMBING IN

When a machine is to be fitted in close proximity to an existing sink unit, you can take advantage of the new style 'SELFBORE' taps and outlet systems now available. These simple and effective D.I.Y. fittings will save both time and money.

In most cases, the fitting of these taps can be done with only a screwdriver and no

① First, unscrew tap and open clamp.

② Fit clamp around copper pipe in required position. Make sure washer is in position.

③ Engage screw and tighten until clamp is secure. <u>Do not</u> <u>over tighten</u>

④ Insert tap assembly into clamp. Ensure tap is in 'off' position.

⑤ Turn clockwise until pipe is penetrated. Set tap to position required.

⑥ Tighten hexagonal nut towards the pipe. This secures tap in position.

⑦ The tap is now ready for use. Connect hose to ¾ BSP thread on tap and turn on.

Plumbing in.

soldering is required. You do not even need to drain or turn off the main water system at all.

At this stage I feel it is better to give you some visual help rather than pages of text. The following pages show you how easy the fitting of such units can be!

DO IT YOURSELF PLUMBING OUT

1. Select the most convenient place in the waste pipe. 1¼" (31mm) or 1½" (38mm) dia.
2. Disconnect components (as shown above). Place saddle halve around waste pipe, removing saddle inserts if pipe is 1½" dia. Ensure that 'O' ring is seated in recess. Tighten screws by stages to give an even and maximum pressure on waste pipe.
3. Insert cutting tool and screw home (clockwise) until hole is cut in waste pipe. Repeat to ensure a clean entry.

Plumbing out.
All components can be unscrewed by turning anti-clockwise.

4. Remove cutter and screw in elbow. Use locking nut ⑤ to determine final position of elbow and tighten, or screw non-return valve ③ directly into saddle piece.

5. To complete installation choose correct size hose coupling to suit drain hose and secure hose with hose clip (not included).

6. It is important to remove regularly lint and other deposits from non-return valve. Simply unscrew retaining collar ④

Discharge into a combined sink and washing machine trap.

This trap allows water from the sink to drain away as normal but has an extra branch for attaching the washing machine hose.

Siroflex anti-syphon unit.

This unit provides an in-line air break to prevent syphonage occurring via your appliance drain hose. Full fitting instructions are supplied with every unit.

Chapter 9

Venting

Many washerdriers and tumbledriers vent the warm moist air which is produced during the drying cycle, into the room in which they are situated. This can amount to several pints of water vapour which will readily condense on the nearest cold surface, i.e. cupboards, windows, etc. Most appliances are situated in the kitchen where a fair amount of moisture is already produced from cooking, so the addition of extra condensation is an unwanted burden resulting in damage to the surrounding areas and also encourages the growth of mould in some situations. Condenser washerdriers and tumbledriers do alleviate this problem although the condenser drier is very costly when compared to ordinary vented tumbledriers.

The answer to the problems caused by ordinary machines is external venting. This may simply be a case of attaching one end of a flexible hose to the vent of the machine and hanging the other end out of an open window (both front and rear venting machines can be vented in this way). Although this solves the problem of moisture condensing in the room, it has its drawbacks, one of which is that there has to be a window near by which can be left open with the hose hanging through for as long as the machine is in use. As the majority of tumbledriers are used mainly in the autumn and

winter leaving a window open may not be convenient. The machine may also be left unattended or used at night on *Economy 7 – either way, it is not wise to leave a window open.

The most convenient way around all these problems is to vent the machine permanently. This is not a difficult procedure, and with the square, through-the-wall vent system as opposed to the large round

A window mounted permanent vent system.

A through the wall vent system showing the new style square ducting which is much easier to fit.

Both through the wall and window fittings take the circular vent hose of the machine and adaptors are available to suit most sizes of hose and machine combinations.

If an anti-draught cover is fitted, make sure it remains clear by checking it regularly for blockages and fluff build-up.

trunking, fitting can be quite simple. As can be seen from the illustrations several variations are available, with ends to fit most popular makes. If a convenient outside wall is not available, the kit can also be used to permanently vent through glass, again avoiding the need to leave windows open. Each kit comes with fitting instructions, but obviously care must be taken to check for hidden pipes or cables prior to making the hole in the masonry.

*Although the setting of domestic appliances to take advantage of off-peak electricity is commonplace, I have reservations about this practice and advocate the use of a smoke detector placed in the vicinity of any machines that are used in this way, as added protection should a serious fault develop whilst the machine is unattended.

POINTS TO REMEMBER

Many combined washerdriers which vent to atmosphere have a removable filter fitted within the exhaust tube which should be cleaned regularly. This is often overlooked because of its inaccessibility, i.e. under worktops, etc. If permanently venting this type of machine, do not forget to remove the filter or it will quickly clog and cause problems.

When sliding a machine with a rear fixed vent hose back into position, make sure that the flexible section of hose does not get flattened between the machine and the wall, thus causing a restriction. Another problem that can occur is that if a hose is fitted which is too long or if a hose is simply pushed through the hole in the wall without using a proper vent kit, either 1. The excess of hose can kink and form U-bends. If moisture condenses on the inner wall of the hose it will collect at such points and effectively block the hose or severely restrict the normal airflow thus reducing drier efficiency, or 2. If pushed through a cavity wall, the soft flexible hose may again form a U-bend, but it could also slip back so that the open end rests within the cavity thus allowing the water vapour expelled during the dry cycle to penetrate the cavity of the wall. All these problems can be avoided by obtaining a suitable kit and installing it correctly.

Chapter 10

Functional testing

Throughout the book, reference is made to functional testing to ensure that the action of the machine is correct and installation is suitable. Use this sequence as a guide to ensuring correct operation after installation, repair or servicing. The purpose is to test where practicable, all functions of the machine and plumbing installation in the most efficient manner. The test will suit most types of machines which use mechanical timers/programmers. Some slight modification may be required to suit model variations. Electronically controlled machines, i.e. non-mechanical timers, will have selectable self- test programmes similar to this sequence. See Timers chapter.

A TYPICAL INSTALLATION AND FUNCTIONAL TEST

1. With machine in its correct operating position and levelled correctly, and with all panels fitted, ensure that both hot and cold taps and power supply socket are turned on.
2. Ensure the door is correctly closed and latched.
3. It is not necessary to put a wash load into the machine or detergent in the dispenser for this type of test.
4. Select a hot wash cycle (90–95 degrees). On most

machines this will only energise the hot fill valve and therefore test the flow rate/pressure supplied to it. The machine should fill to low level within four minutes if the water pressure is adequate. If the fill time is over this period check that the hot supply tap is fully on. In most instances little can be done for slow hot filling, (See – Basics – Plumbing) and will in general cause only minor problems such as failing to dispense powders effectively from the drawer. In severe cases either connect to cold supply with a 'Y'-joint or alternatively, the powder could quite simply be sprinkled over the wash load in the drum, (only if the wash is to be started immediately), still allowing the machine to take the hot fill at its reduced rate.
Note: Some machines can be modified internally. Instruction for this will be given in the accompanying user handbook/installation document supplied with the machine. Follow the instructions given and do not attempt alteration without the detailed instructions of the manufacturer. As with any repair, inspection or maintenance, isolate the machine thoroughly prior to removing any panels.
5. Check for drum action when machine has filled to low level. Some machines may require the timer to be advanced slightly to

avoid a paused heat-only cycle before drum rotation takes place. See – Timer chapter (Thermostop). Check for clockwise and counter-clockwise drum action.
6. Check that door interlock operates and that door will not open during this cycle.
7. Switch the machine off and move it to the special treatments (fabric conditioner) position. This will select a higher level fill via the cold valve. Some machines will possess a choice of the positions for this – one before the short or delicates spin and one before the normal or fast spin. Remember on delicate cycles the machine will stop full of water after the special treatments cycle and will only move on to the spin when instructed. Each machine has its own way of impulsing to the spin from this 'hold' position so make yourself aware from your handbook. See also – Machine will not empty chapter.
7a. If you choose the position prior to the normal spin, the machine will fill to its high level using the cold valve and therefore a check of the cold inlet can be made. Wait four minutes maximum for the high level to be reached. As the cold inlet pressure is usually governed by the street mains to the house the pressure is normally well above the minimum required.
8. When the high level is reached check for rotation, again clockwise and counter-clockwise.
9. As the programme of Special Treatments is short, allow the machine to impulse normally to the pump out stage. (If delicate cycle, use the normal advance mechanism). Check that the machine empties within one minute or thereabouts (verifying that the pump rate and outlet are correct).
10. Allow the machine to impulse on to the spin and through to the off position. Time and spin speeds will differ

depending on whether special treatments cycle or whichever spin speed was selected.

11. Check immediately after the off position has been reached to see if entry to the machine is correctly inhibited by the interlock.

12. Time the delay of the interlock, minimum one minute up to two minutes. Check that after such time the door can be opened correctly. Do not be impatient and force the latch mechanism or handle.

13. Next, select a drying programme. Reference to the manufacturer's instruction booklet will be required as machines differ in the way they are set.

14. During the cycle, check for drum rotation clockwise and counter-clockwise, blower motor operation (background noise), warming up of door glass (do not touch the door glass directly as some makes get extremely hot). On condenser type machines, check also for intermittent pump action. Do not allow the dry sequence to continue for too long without a load in. With vented washerdriers, check the rear vent (or if a vent hose system is fitted check hose) for free flow of warm air.

15. Move the drier timer to the cool tumble position (i.e. five minutes before end of drying programme), and allow the sequence to finish. This allows both drum and heater unit to cool correctly whilst confirming correct operation of dryer timer.

This simple sequence is likely to take 10–15 minutes. If at any point a fault should occur, the correct action can be implemented.

These simple steps have in effect, confirmed (or otherwise) the operation of both water valves and pressure supplied to them, the pressure system for water level control, hoses and seals, outlet pump and waste, programmer (though not in depth), spin speed, drier blower motor (if fitted), heater and drier timer. However, what this relatively simple test has not shown is whether the wash heater works or if the wash thermostat operates correctly. To confirm this, the time taken to heat up should be noted, also the correct impulse from the thermostat for that particular programme setting. These two items will be tested on the next full wash cycle after the basic functional test proves satisfactory. It is therefore advisable to check both heater and correct temperature advancing on a normal wash cycle.

Chapter 11

Locating a fault

Whenever possible the symptoms of the fault should be confirmed by the operation of the machine up to the point of the suspected fault using the appropriate test sequence, whereupon the machine should be stopped, disconnected from the mains supply and the relevant flowchart or fault sequence followed. For major leaks, blown fuses, etc., this is not practical (more damage may result by repeated operation of the machine). In these cases, the fault is known and further confirmation would be of little benefit. Continuing to use a machine with a known fault may in fact, result in further damage to the machine or its surroundings.

Being able to assess and locate a fault may at first seem a difficult thing to do, but if a few simple procedures are carried out prior to starting the work, they will help cut down on the time spent on the machine. Hopping in a random fashion from one part of the machine to another, hoping that you will come across the fault and subsequently repair it, is hardly the best approach to repair work. This is not the way to tackle any job. Without doubt, the best method of fault finding is to be gained from your own experience of the machine, the fault with it and its location and rectification based on all the available information. Always remember a methodical approach to the work in hand, saves time and effort by eliminating unnecessary replacements based on guesswork.

However there are a few things that can be done before such testing. These will ascertain if, in fact, it is the machine itself that is at fault or if an external/user fault is the source. Indeed, a large percentage of repair calls, are in fact, not a fault of the machine at all. Before jumping to conclusions, pause for a moment. You will not only save time and effort, but money as well.

Remember these points when starting a repair.
1. Allow yourself enough time to complete the task in hand.
2. Do not cut corners at the expense of safety.
3. Try to ensure adequate working space wherever possible.
4. Make notes about the position of the part/s to be removed, the colours and position of wires, bolts, etc.

If you can acquire this practice, it will help you in all repairs that you carry out, not only with your washing machine or tumbledrier.

A few simple checks.
(a) CHECK – That the machine is turned on at the socket.
(b) CHECK – That the fuse in the plug is intact and working. This can be checked by replacing the suspected fuse with one out of a working item of the same rating.
(c) CHECK – That the taps are in the ON position.
(d) CHECK – That the door is closed correctly, and that a wash cycle is selected and the knob or switch has been pulled/pushed to the ON position.
(e) CHECK – That the machine is not on a 'RINSE HOLD' position. This on mast machines will cause the machine to stand idle until instructed to do otherwise.

If the fault still remains, the next stop is to determine its true nature, and subsequent repair.

Chapter 12

General care and attention

For many repairs it is best that the machine is laid on its front face or side. Generally it is best to lay the machine on the side opposite the timer. (The timer is located directly behind the main programme knob.) This is to avoid the tub and drum assembly coming in contact with the timer.

Always ensure that the outer shell of the machine in protected with a suitable cover when attempting to lay the machine down. The machine should be lowered slowly, to avoid excessive movement of the suspension. When lowering the machine, it is a good idea to place a strip of wood under the top edge of the machine, to provide room for the fingers for lifting the machine back into its correct position after the repair.

When laying the machine over, care should be taken to protect oneself from injury. Firstly, ensure that the machine is completely disconnected from the main supply, and that the inlet and outlet hoses are removed. Secondly, before attempting to lay the machine over, decide if you need any help. These machines are very heavy and a little help may prevent a slipped disc! Thirdly, before attempting to move the machine, ensure that the floor is dry. A wet floor has no grip, especially if the water is soapy.

The correct rating of fuse must be used as per the manufacturer's instructions. As a general guide, the applications for the three main ratings of fuse are listed in the general safety guide section.

REGULAR INSPECTION POINTS

A regular internal inspection of your machines may enable you to identify a part that may not be working correctly, or find a perished hose before a leak occurs. It is recommended that the following points be checked regularly.

Inspect	When	Special notes
Pump filter (if fitted)	Weekly	As per manufacturer's manual. Often depends on usage.
Vent filter (if fitted)	After every dry cycle	Must be kept clean for efficient drying.
Valve filters (hot & cold)	6 months	If dirty, pull out carefully with pliers and wash.
Door seal	6 months	If seal is tacky to the touch it may need to be renewed soon.
Door glass		Remove sticky fluff or scale deposits from door glass inner surface with non-abrasive pad. Check inlet duct for cracking.
All hoses	6 months	Ensure that all corrugations in all hoses are checked thoroughly.
Pump and sump hose catch pot	6 months	Check for items that may have collected in or at these points. Remove as necessary.

Condenser unit (if fitted)	6 months or as required	Check for fluff build up in fan chamber and ducting. Some makes are more prone than others to problems. Also dependent on usage.
Suspension	6 months	Check suspension mounts on tub and body of machine. If slide type, see suspension section.
Motor brushes (if fitted)	6 months or yearly	Check for wear and/or sticking in slides. Renew if below half normal length.
Belt tension	6 months or yearly	Check and adjust belt tension if necessary. See Belts chapter.
Level machine	Yearly/after every repair	Check that the machine is standing firmly on the floor and does not rock. Adjust by unscrewing adjustable feet or packing under the wheels.
Check plug and connectors	Before and after every repair	After repair look for poor connections in the plug and socket. Also look for any cracks or other damage. Renew as necessary.
Taps and washers	Before and after every repair	Check taps for free movement, corrosion and/or leaks.

Note: For inspection points on dry only machines, see chapter on Dry-only machines (tumbledriers).

Chapter 13

Determining the fault

Throughout the manual, flowcharts are used to aid the fault finding process. The location of faults will become much easier as you become more conversant with your machine.

Selecting the correct flowchart or fault guide for the job will be made easier if it is remembered that faults fall into three main categories, mechanical, electrical and chemical.

Mechanical faults will normally become apparent by a change in the usual operational noise level of the machine. For instance a faulty suspension may cause a banging or bumping noise. A broken or slipping belt (incorrect tension) may give rise to excessive spin noise or little or no drum rotation. This may also indicate a drum or motor bearing fault.

Electrical faults fall into two major categories

Impulse path faults
A fault is classed as an impulse fault when an internal, pre-determined instruction has failed, i.e. thermostat does not close or open at the required temperature, or the timer fails to move on after a given time sequence.

Component faults
A fault is classed as a component fault when a complete unit has failed. If, for

instance, the pump, heater or motor should fail, the fault is said to be a component fault. Not all component faults are readily apparent. For instance, a failure in the coil of the water valve supplying the condenser unit would manifest itself as a failure of the machine to dry the clothes. The wash cycles would be unaffected and all obvious functions of the dry cycle such

as heating up, circulation of air (noise of motor) etc., would appear to be OK, but with no water to cool the condenser, drying could not take place. This highlights the need not only to understand the basic function of each item but its relationship with others. Read all sections of the book thoroughly to help in understanding the way in which items function together. Full comprehension of all aspects will assist you greatly in determining the cause of the trouble from symptoms displayed by the machine.

Chemical faults
These are normally associated with the powder being used and will cover such problems as poor washing, scaling problems, blocking, etc. A comprehensive guide to washing problems and useful hints will be found at the rear of this manual, in the chapter – Common causes of poor washing results.

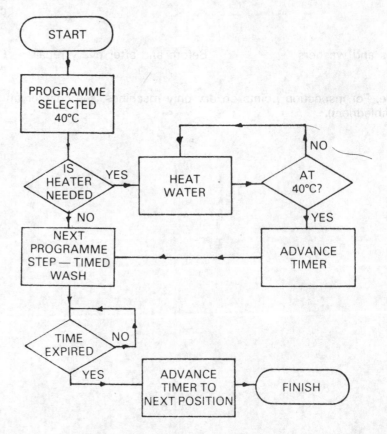

Shown is a simplified flowchart of the operation described.

Fault finding reference guide – wash cycle

Machine will not work at all

Basics
Locating a fault
Interlocks

Machine will not fill/take powder

Basics
Locating a fault
Inlet valve fault finding

Machine leaks
Emergency procedures
Locating a fault
Leaks fault finding

Pressure systems
Pumps
Motor speeds
Inlet valve fault finding
Suspension

Machine does not wash clean
Locating a fault
Main drive belt (tension)
Common causes of poor wash results
Basic plumbing
Pump

Machine will not empty
Emergency procedures
Locating a fault
Pumps
Basic plumbing
Harness faults

Machine is noisy
Noise faults
Drum bearings
Main motor
Suspension

Machine washes but no spin

Locating a fault
Interlocks
Pumps
Main motor
Main motor speed control

Machine won't move through programme
Basic plumbing
Thermostats
Heater
Inlet valve fault finding
Programmer/timer

Machine will not turn drum

Check drive belt
Main motor
Main motor speed control
Interlocks

Machine sticks through programme
Locating a fault
Basic plumbing
Pump
Inlet valve fault finding
Programmer/timer

Machine spins on all positions
Locating a fault
Module control
Main motor
Programmer/timer

Machine blows fuses
Emergency procedures
General safety guide
Basics
Low insulation

The lists below the main fault headings indicate the sequence with which they should be examined.

Fault finding reference guide – dry cycle

Fault	Check
No drying cycle	Check for correct setting Own instruction booklet Basics – Electrical Basics – Plumbing Door switches (Interlocks) Wiring harness faults
Poor drying of clothes	Check load size. See: Own instruction booklet and How They Work section Basics – Electrical Basics – Plumbing Drying components – faults Air ducts/motors, i.e. main wash, pump and fan Heaters (airflow type) Thermostats Timers – both main and auxiliary (drier) Harness faults
No heat at all on dry cycle	Air ducts (blockages). See Drying components chapter Heaters (airflow type) Thermostats and T.O.C.s Timers
Heat too high	Check setting. See: own instruction booklet Air ducts (blockages) Motors (fan motor) Thermostats Harness connections Timer (drier)

NOISE FAULTS

Noise can be one of the first signs that something is going wrong with your washing machine. Noise faults are easily ignored, subsequently over a length of time they can be accepted as the norm, because of this it is important that noise faults be examined immediately.

As with other faults, noise faults become easier to locate the more conversant that you become with your machine.

NOISES AND THEIR MOST COMMON LOCATIONS

A loud grating or rumbling noise would indicate a main drum bearing fault. See the Bearings chapter.

A loud high pitched noise would indicate a main motor bearing or pump bearing fault. See the chapters on Motors and Pumps.

A noise just before and after spin, would indicate wear or water penetration of the suspension mounts. See the chapter on Suspension.

A squeaking noise mainly during the wash cycle, would indicate a poorly adjusted drive belt. Instructions on how to adjust the drive belt appear in the chapter on Belts.

Noise on the dry cycle may indicate a blockage in the fan housing, perhaps a build up of fluff or distortion of moulding, etc. See: Drying components chapter. A more metallic or grating noise could denote a failure of one or both bearings of the fan motor. Such faults may be accompanied by intermittent operation of the motor due to jamming, poor/lengthy drying or too high a temperature during the dry cycle caused by a reduction in air flow as the fan rotates slowly, See: Motors chapter.

A rather unusual though not uncommon fault can be found on machines with cast aluminium pulleys. If a crack or break develops in one leg/spoke of the pulley, a noise very similar to that of main bearing failure can be heard. Check such pulleys closely for this type of defect and also for tight fit on shaft of drum. These should not be a loose fit. See: Bearing chapter. This type of fault may be apparent on wash, spin and dry cycles alike.

COIN DAMAGE

Coins and other metal items are easily trapped in the machine, and can cause a great deal of damage. They can become trapped between the inner drum and outer tub, and should be removed before damage to the drum occurs.

Coin damage can be identified by small bumps on the inner drum or a rattling noise when spinning. On early enamel drums, this may be accompanied by small flakes of enamel in the wash load. It is not uncommon on machines with stainless steel drums for the drum to be torn open by coin damage. Take care when checking the drum interior for this kind of damage as the torn metal edges can be extremely sharp. In such instances the inner drum will need to be renewed as a repair is not possible. Small pips of plastic found in the wash load may indicate the presence of a coin or similar item trapped between the inner and outer tub.

Where there is no damage to the drum, it may be possible to avoid a full stripdown/removal by removing the coin from the drum/tub gap by removing the heater, see: Heater section. The item can either be removed via this opening, or manoeuvred into the sump hose, where it can be extracted easily. To refit the heater, See: Heaters chapter. **Note:** Any large items such as bra wires or keys can be removed via the heater opening avoiding the sharp 90 degree angle into the sump hose. All such problems could of course be avoided by first removing all items from pockets before washing. This simple action can save a lot of time and money in the long run.

Typical coin damage to a drum. This kind of fault can be easily avoided by careful checking of pockets, etc., prior to loading the washer. If this type of damage has been caused, the only cure is to carry out a complete drum renewal.

Typical damage caused by coin damage to an outer tub. Although this does not seem as bad as the damage to the previous drum photograph, the chips on the enamel will cause corrosion.
To cure this type of damage, treat the affected areas with an anti-corrosion compound. This is readily available in motorists' shops and is generally used for minor car bodywork repairs. When applying the above compound, please ensure that the manufacturer's instructions are followed carefully, and that the compound does not come into contact with rubber hoses or seals, etc. Always use this type of substance in a well ventilated area.
Stainless steel or plastic tubs are not generally affected by this type of damage, although regular inspection is important.
Do not apply anti-corrosion compound to plastic tubs.

Chapter 14

Leaks – fault finding

The leaks described in this chapter relate equally to wash-only machines, vented washerdriers and condenser washerdriers. Additional problems can be found with the extra hoses, connections and seals found in condenser machines, and reference to the Drying Components chapter will be required. Specific problem areas on such systems are: 1. poor positioning of hoses resulting in chafing, 2. poor connection of rubber hoses to moulded plastic condenser units resulting in difficult to isolate faults, 3. lack of heat resistant sealant (from earlier repairs) in areas such as heat duct to door seal inlet, fan chamber to both heat duct and condenser unit.

Ensure all connections are secure and correctly positioned and all the protective covers and sleeves are in good condition. Seal hose connections and condenser mouldings and ducts with the correct sealants, see Useful tips and information and Drying components chapters.

With the above in mind, the flowchart can be followed. At first it may seem obvious where the leak is coming from, but it would still be wise to follow the flowchart through.

Box 1: The smallest of holes in the door boot (door seal) can be the cause of the biggest leaks. The seal should also be checked and replaced if any

holes are found or if it feels sticky or tacky to the touch. The contact between the door glass and the seal should be a good one, with no scaling or fluff adhering to the door glass. If any scale, etc., is found on the glass it can be easily removed by rubbing gently with a non abrasive scouring pad. Details of door seal replacement can be found in the chapter on Door seal fitting.

Box 2: The clamp band that secures the door seal to the washer should be checked for tightness. Details of different types of clamp bands can be found in the chapter Door seal fitting.

Box 3: The dispenser hose is located at the base of the soap dispenser, and forms the flexible connection with the tub. Again, thorough inspection of this hose is advised, as most of the water that the machine uses passes via this hose, and can therefore lead to some quite large leaks. This hose is usually a grommet type fitting, and should be checked for tightness, i.e. it should not rotate, A sign of a bad fit is scaling/powder marks running down the outer tub at the fitting point. If the hose feels sticky or tacky to the touch, it should be replaced.
Note: If this hose has leaked, the water would have contained detergent. If the water has come into contact with the suspension legs it may cause a loud squeaking/grinding noise just before and after the spin. (This fault is more pronounced on Hoover automatics.) This is because the suspension works its hardest at this time. Please refer to the chapter on Suspension.

If your make of washer has a hose connected between the outer tub and the rear of the machine, this is called an air vent tube. This in itself cannot leak as no water passes through it, although it may be used if the machine overfoamed, overfilled or has spun whilst still full of water. The hose is of the grommet fitting type, and should be checked for perishing as before. Most modern

Exposed view of typical basic drum assembly. For additions to this basic arrangement, refer to accompanying schematic drawing and drier components section.
1. *Door seal (door boot).*
2. *Clamp band.*
3. *Spring fastening for clamp band (could be bolt or rubber garter type).*
4. *Front tub weight size and position may vary.*
5. *Tub lip for door seal to locate onto.*
6. *Dispenser hose.*
7. *Dispenser hose clip.*
8. *Outer tub. Position of tub weights vary.*
9. *Top tub weights. Locations vary.*
10. *Carbon face seal for main bearing.*
11. *Front drum bearings (ball bearing type).*
12. *Front bearing spacer.*
13. *Rear bearing spacer.*
14. *Rear bearing (ball bearing type).*
15. *Securing clip (spring type).*
16. *Drum spider (detachable version).*
17. *Spider fixing bolt.*
18. *Spider washer and spacer.*
19. *Drum pulley.*
20. *Drum pulley fixing bolt and locking tab.*
21. *Pressure vessel hose.*
22. *Pressure vessel hose clip (spring combination clips).*
23. *Heater.*
24. *Rear tub seal (back half seal).*
25. *Backhalf casting.*
26. *Thermostat grommet.*
27. *Suspension unit (spring damper type).*

machines use the soap dispenser as the air vent as well as the water inlet, thus eliminating an extra grommet fitting hose in manufacture.

Box 4: The sump hose is the flexible hose located at the bottom of the machine. Depending on the make and model of your appliance, this will be in one of two configurations, (a) Linking the pump and the tub. (b) Linking the filter and tub, with a separate hose linking the filter and pump, thus creating a trap for any foreign objects to prevent them reaching the pump.

Again this should be checked for perishing and replaced if found to be tacky or sticky. The grommet fittings should also be checked, as explained in Box 3, and the clips should be checked for tightness as explained in the Pumps chapter. If the machine is the type with a filter fitted, all hoses to and from the filter housing and the filter seal should be checked for defects. At this point it would be advisable to thoroughly check the pump as detailed in the Pumps chapter.

Box 5: The thermostat and heater seal are both generally located on the back half or underside of the outer tub, depending on the make and model of the machine. An exception to this rule is the Hotpoint front loader, where the thermostat, heater and pressure vessel are located on the front of the outer tub, directly below the door seal. Access to these components is gained by the removal of the front panel of the machine. Details of this are to be found in the Door seal fitting chapter.

If the heater seal is found to be leaking, it can sometimes be stopped by tightening the centre nut. This increase the width of the rubber seal by squashing it 'vice like'. If the leak persists at this point, the heater will have to be changed completely, as

Fig. 4. A simplified diagram of a combined washerdrier:
A. Soap dispenser.
B. Heaters housed in heater ducting.
C. Fan and motor for air circulation.
D. Cold water inlet to condenser unit.
E. Door seal with inlet for heater duct.
F. Outer tub unit.
G. Inner drum.
H. Outlet pump.
I. Condenser unit.
J. Outlet hose.

the seal is not available as a separate item.

Box 6: The connections between the pressure switches and the tub should be checked now, as detailed in the Water level control chapter.

Box 7: The hoses and clips on the inlet valves should now be checked in conjunction with the

Water inlet valves chapter. On some valves there is a slight chance that the top of the valve can split. This is often shown by a small brown rust patch on the top of the valve.

Box 8: The tub seal and grommets are to be checked now. This means the seal or seals that fit between the separate parts of the main tub assembly. In addition to these seals, small rubber grommets may be found. These will have been fitted to block 'machine holes' that are used in the manufacture of the machine. If these come out or leak, they should be replaced or have sealant applied to them. If the large tub seals leak they should also be renewed. This type of repair is described in the Bearings chapter.

Box 9: Any corrosion or flaking of the enamel covering of the outer tub can be treated with a good brand of rust inhibitor, taking care that it does not come into contact with any of the internal rubber hoses, seals, etc., and is used in conjunction with the manufacturer's instructions. Places to note, are where the brackets for the motor and the suspension are welded on to the outer tub. These are stress points where the enamel may crack and flake, allowing rust to form. By the time a leak has started at these points, it is too late to save the outer tub, and it must be renewed completely if a lasting repair is to be made. Check plastic outer tubs closely for cracks. It is felt that the occurrence of tub renewal on today's modern automatics, is very rare, therefore, the need for a lengthy section in this book would be unnecessary. Also, the cost of such items and all the relevant seals and parts necessary to complete such a repair may not be cost effective.

If the machine still leaks after these checks, please refer to the following chapters, Basic – Plumbing and Motors (speed control).

Chapter 15

Machine will not empty

Of all the faults reported, this must be one of the most common. Often this fault and the 'leak' fault are one of the same. The reason for this being that on many machines there is no 'spin inhibit system'. This is especially true of older machines, or machines that are produced abroad. If there is no spin inhibit system, it means that if for any reason the machine cannot empty, it will still try to spin. The consequences of this action, is that the increased drum speed pressurises the inner tub, causing leaks from soap dispensers, air vent hoses and door seals. Thus one fault can cause several problems. On most later machines and many of the machines currently produced in Britain, the level switch inhibits (stops) the machine before the spin if a level of water is detected. This means that if there is water in the machine, the pressure causes the switch to move to the OFF position, therefore not allowing the machine to spin. For a more detailed description of the pressure switch, please refer to the Water level control chapter.

The 'not emptying' fault can fall into three main categories, blockage, mechanical fault or electrical fault.

Box 1: Follow the emergency procedure for removing the water already trapped inside the machine.

Box 2: Check the outlet and sump hoses, as well as the outlet filter (if fitted). If a blockage or a kink has been found, remove it and refit the pipe(s) and filter.

Box 3: The pump is located at the machine end of the outlet hose, and junction of the sump hose. The small chamber should be checked for blockages, the impeller should be checked for free rotation, and that it hasn't come adrift from its mounting

This vented type combined machine has a rinse hold button 2nd from the left. This may be correctly causing a spin inhibit, check your instruction booklet for correct operation and use.

This combined condenser washerdrier machine clearly indicates the no spin option 3rd button from the left. However, errors in setting can still occur, always double check.

to the pump motor shaft. If the impeller is adrift from the shaft, no water would be pumped although the motor itself would run. A quick way to check the connection of the shaft and impeller is to hold the shaft whilst trying to turn the impeller. If all is well, they should only turn in unison. Remember to turn anti-clockwise, otherwise the impeller will unscrew from the shaft. If a fault is found at this point, refer to the Pump chapter.

Box 3A: If no blockage is found in the section above, and the bearings are not suspected, the stator continuity of the pump windings must be checked. Please refer to the Using a meter chapter.

Box 4: At this point, the outlet hose should be checked again. An internal blockage such as a coin or button can act as a type of valve, and be very difficult to see. The best method of checking this is to connect the hose to a standard tap, observing the flow of water.

Box 5: The final step is to check the wiring harness connections. Please refer to the Wiring and harness faults chapter.

MACHINE WILL NOT EMPTY FLOWCHART

Chapter 16

Door seal fitting

There are many types of door seal available, depending on make, model and the age of your machine. The removal and fitting of three typical door seals (without heater ducting connections) is shown. The models used in this example are Hoover, Bendix and Hotpoint. They are used to illustrate the principles which are basically the same for all machines. The combined washerdrier machines may or may not have this addition of a heater duct entry point connection. This will be dependent on make and model of your machine. See photographs of various types of door seal and ducting. The door seal bridges the gap between the outer tub and the shell of the machine, and in most washerdriers is used as a convenient entry point for the air inlet duct (although not always so). The flexible rubber seal provides access to the inner drum via the door opening for loading the machine and inlet point for the heater duct during the drying cycle (on some machines), whilst also giving a watertight seal to the door glass. The seal should be renewed if found to be perished or holed at any point, paying special attention to the folds and mounting of the door seal. The air inlet duct rubber moulding (if fitted) should be inspected closely for signs of cracking and hardening due to heat damage and check also

that it is correctly seated and sealed with the correct sealant (if required).

There are three ways that a door seal is secured to the outer tub, all very similar in concept. On the outer tub there is a formed lip. When the rubber seal is located onto this lip, it is then held in position by a large clamp band, and pressure exerted by the band to create a water-tight seal. There are several versions of clamp bands used in today's machines. Four of the most common are described below. The majority of machines will have one or a combination of those listed whereas the others may have a variation of one of those described. Use this list to help identify the type used in your machine.

1. A simple metal band secured by a bolt, which when tightened reduces the diameter of the band.
2. As (1), but the open ends of the band are secured by a spring.
3. This method is best described as a large rubber band or spring joined together to form an expanding ring. Both types are called garter rings. When fitted correctly, the ring rests in a recess in the door seal, which in turn rests in the recess of the tub lip, therefore creating the watertight seal. Unlike the previous two methods, this band cannot be

slackened by the loosening of a bolt or spring, and is best removed by prising the garter ring from its position in the seal recess by using a flat-bladed screwdriver to lift it over the lip. The best way to refit a rubber or spring garter ring is to locate the bottom of the ring in the recess of the fitted door seal slowly working the ring inside the recess in an upward direction with both hands meeting at the top. This can be likened to fitting a tyre onto a bicycle wheel after mending a puncture.
4. A slightly unusual fastening may be encountered where both ends of a wire band are joined by a small metal plate. The ends of the wire band are linked into two holes in the metal plate. The plate has a larger hole/slot in it and if a small screwdriver is inserted into this slot and forms a tight fit, when turned, a 'cam' action occurs which reduces or increases the overall circumference. Only a small movement is required, approximately a quarter turn between open and closed. When closed correctly, the plate will lock into position. Access to the plate can be gained through the door latch hole after first removing the two interlock fixing screws. This type of fixing is mainly found on machines in the Colston/Ariston range. The reason for this type of clamp band is that access to the more usual clamp band would be impossible due to a close front fitting circular concrete tub weight which surrounds the door seal tub lip. **Note:** To aid the fitting of a door seal, a little washing up liquid may be applied to the tub lip or the door seal tub lip moulding. (Not on the front shell lip.) This will allow the rubber to slip more easily into position on the metal or plastic lip of the outer tub.

As described earlier, many modern washerdrier machines vent the warm air into the drum of the machine via a preformed extension of the door seal which fits around the lower portion of the heating duct. It is essential that the door seal is positioned correctly on the tub lip in order to allow the duct and seal to fit neatly without any distortion. It is most important that this union is correctly fitted and sealed to avoid the possible leak of water or vapour. Various fixings can be found which secure the door seal to the heater duct. Sealant is often applied in the manufacturing process to help fit parts together and to fill in any gaps left between the door seal and any irregularities that may be present. If your machine had sealant used in manufacture, it is essential that it is renewed whenever the door seal is renewed or whenever the ducting is removed or stripped down for any reason. Only the correct heat resistant sealant should be used, see: Useful Tips and Information chapter. Do not use the general purpose sealant which is used for water-tight seals on hoses and pressure systems. The fitting of the door seal to the shell of the machine is similar to the tub lip system in that three major variations are found:

(a) The most straightforward seal simply grips the shell lip with no other added support other than the elasticity of the door seal itself on early machines. For safety reasons modern machines now use various methods of secondary fixing to prevent the door seal being easily removed or dislodged from the shell lip. It is essential that such fixings are replaced if they have once been removed for any reason.

(b) This type also uses the shell lip, with the aid of a clamp band. A recess is formed on the outer edge of the seal for a clamp band or clamp wire to be inserted. This ensures a firm grip on the shell lip. As with the inner tub lip, many variations can be found.

(c) The third method involves a plastic flange that is screwed on to the outside of the shell. The screws that hold this flange pass through a recess in the outer front lip of the door seal therefore securing it firmly to the front panel. Variations on both of the later clamps can be found on modern machines. All are fitted as a safety measure to restrict access to the inner of the machine. It is essential that any such fixing is replaced correctly if it has had to be removed for any reason. Before removing the old door seal a simple examination of the old seal and a note of its correct positioning will aid the subsequent repair and renewal as the new seal will need to fit in exactly the same position. Some door seals have a definite top and bottom, or preshaped sections for door hinges or catches, etc., and will fit no other way. **Remember:** It is easier to line up the seal before fitting rather than trying to adjust the seal when the clamp bands have been fitted. **Note:**

Some machines have one or more of their tub weights mounted on the front section of the outer tub, encircling the door seal and tub clamp fitting, leaving little or no access to the clamp or tub lip. However, do not remove the front tub weight to aid door seal fitting as it is not necessary for most machines, e.g. Creda, Zanussi, Ariston and Bendix, etc., even though some have front tub weights surrounding the tub clamp bands. The Zanussi and Creda seals can be changed through the door opening in the front panel of the machine, without removing the top at all. (Having said this, removing the top of the machine will provide more light, – remove if necessary). The way in which the door seal of washerdrier machines fits to both outer tub and shell are identical to wash only machines i.e. lip and clamp. Fitting however will be found from clamp plate to clamp spring. Refitting therefore will be a reversal of the removal process.

REMOVAL OF TYPICAL DOOR SEAL (HOOVER)

1. Check door glass inner for scale deposit ridge and clean off with non-abrasive pad.

2. Grasp door seal firmly and pull downwards to free from shell lip. Some machines may have clamp band on front lip. Remove this first.

3. When freed from lip, continue pulling in a downward direction.

6. With position of clamp band and bolt in view proceed to remove band. Free seal from the clip as shown above.

8. View showing inner lip moulding and ridge. The ridge is fitted at the 9 o'clock position when viewed from the front of the machine.

4. Free complete door seal from the front lip and allow seal to rest on inner side of front panel.

7. New door seal of type to be fitted to the machine shown.

9. Cutaway view of a typical door seal to show intricate moulding and positioning of tub and shell lips of the seal.

REMOVAL OF A BENDIX DOOR SEAL

5. With top removed, free the top support springs or tie, and lean outer tub unit back as far as possible.

1. Remove the plastic flanges around the door seal front.

2. Remove the door seal from the front lip.

3. Showing the position of the clamp band with the top of the machine removed.

6. View showing the tub lip and weight block gap. (Clean off any scale and/or deposit on the tub lip before fitting the new seal).

7. New door seal checked prior to fitting and smeared with a little washing up liquid to help slide it into position. (Inner lip only).

4. Picture showing the orientation of the band inside the machine. Must be re-fitted in the same position.

8. Ensure that the three drain holes on the door seal are fitted at the bottom of the tub lip

REMOVAL OF A HOTPOINT FRONT LOADER DOOR SEAL

5. Slacken off tub clamp band bolt and remove old door seal.

1. Remove outer plastic surround screws, and top and bottom section.

2. Pull seal to release from shell lip, hinge and catch.

3. Unscrew the timer knob centre and remove the timer knob. Also remove the two front facia fixing screws found behind the timer knob.

5. With the front facia removed, remove the screws securing the front panel of the machine.

7. Remove door switch assembly and pressure switch bracket.

4. Pull out the soap dispenser drawer completely and remove the front facia fixing screws.

6. Four hexagonal headed screws secure the front panel under the bottom edge. (On later machines, three Philips headed screws will be found).

8. With front panel removed, the clamp band can easily be removed.

9. Note the position of hinge and catch mouldings. The door seal can then be pulled free from the tub lip.

10. When fitting a new seal to the tub lip, the tub gap can be adjusted slightly. (Note: the inner lip of the door seal is ribbed).

11. When the new seal is fitted in this position, check that the inner drum rotates without fouling the door seal inner. Adjust if necessary to obtain the smallest gap possible before refitting.

14. With front panel secured, fit the door seal to the front panel lip.

15. Lubricate the hinge and catch points with a little washing up liquid, and ease into position.

12. With new door seal in this position it is wise to check that all of the leads, hoses and pressure vessel are correct before refitting the front panel.

16. Refit plastic surround and ensure that the ends locate correctly. The plastic pips can be moved to aid fitting. The machine is now ready for the functional test.

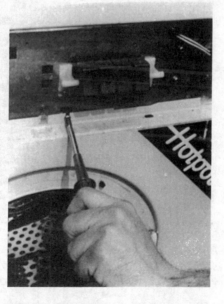

13. Refit front panel, door catch and all front panel fixings.

17. When fitted, the new seal should not have undue kinks or twists. It is essential that this is correctly fitted.

A.

D.

E.

Washerdrier door seals with heater duct inlet protrusions. A. Fagor. B. Ariston. C. Hoover. D. Candy (with removable integral duct seal). E. Candy seal detailing duct seal.

B.

1.

C.

2.

Photo 1 & 2 shows type of sealant sometimes used to secure door seal to heater duct inlet. If originally used, it must be renewed if disturbed or when fitting a new door seal, etc.

The front lip of this door seal is secured by a wire and spring type fixing (No2). Carefully insert a flat bladed screwdriver to ease fixing from its position as shown (shown with door removed for photographic purposes only).

Not all washerdrier machines use the door seal for the heater duct entry point. This early Hotpoint machine has a normal door seal, air inlet is via a fixed outer tub fitment.

Access to the door seal from the top of the machine may be limited in many combined washerdriers such as this Philips machine. With a little thought and planning, however, fitting can be easily carried out.

When removed from the shell of the machine this Zanussi washerdrier tub assembly clearly shows the large tub weight completely encircling the door seal. This type of seal is held in place by a garter spring (type 3). Removal and refitting of both seal and securing band can be carried out with the unit in situ. The unit is shown removed from the machine for photographic purposes only.

Chapter 17

Water inlet valves

INLET VALVE FAULT FINDING

In this section we deal with several of the most common reported faults such as not taking powder, not filling at all, not filling in certain parts of the programme and condenser water supply. Please refer to the flowchart accompanying this chapter.

Many configurations of water valve can be found from single hot or cold to much larger units consisting of three or more individually operated valves grouped together to control the flow to several outlets from one inlet. All inlet point threads are the same size, but outlet hose connections from the valve may differ. A wide variety of fixing brackets are also used, outlet angles can be in-line (classed as 180 degree valves) or angles downwards (classed as 90 degree valves). Operation of the electro-mechanical action follows and covers the general operation of all such valves regardless of size or fixing styles, etc.

A Solenoid coil of some 3 – 5000 ohms (3-5KΩ) resistance when energised (i.e. supplied with power), creates a strong magnetic field at its centre. This field attracts up into the coil a soft iron rod or plunger, and will hold it in that position as long as power is supplied to the coil.

When power is removed (de-energised) from the coil, a spring at the top of the plunger recess returns to its resting position.

HOW DOES IT WORK?

Shown here in detail are the two states of the water valve. With no power supplied to the solenoid coil (a), the soft iron core (b) is pressed firmly onto the centre hole of the flexible diaphragm by spring (c). As chamber (d) is only at atmospheric pressure and the water is at least 4 p.s.i. (somewhat higher), pressure is exerted on the top of the diaphragm*, effectively closing it tight. The greater the water pressure the greater the closing effect of the valve therefore no water will flow.

When power is supplied to the solenoid coil, the resulting magnetic attraction of the coil overcomes the power of the spring (c) and pulls the plunger up into the coil centre. This allows an imbalance of pressure to occur by exposing the centre hole of the diaphragm. The imbalance lifts the flexible diaphragm and allows water to flow into chamber (d), thus water flow is achieved.

It is easier for the water to lift the diaphragm than to balance the pressure by flowing through the very small bleed hole. Any enlargement or blockage of this vital bleed hole will render the valve inoperative.

*The pressure on top of the diaphragm is via a small bleed hole marked (e). It is essential that this very small hole is not obstructed. Though very small, it is a major factor in the correct operation of these types of pressure operated valves.

ELECTRICAL SPADE

RETURN SPRING (c)

PLUNGER (B)

ELECTRO MAGNET (A)

BLEED HOLE (E)

DIAPHRAGM

INLET FILTER

NO WATER TO MACHINE

PRESSURE REDUCER INSERT

(D)

De-energized valve.

ELECTRICAL SPADE

A

PLUNGER
(LIFTED)

B

E

RETURN SPRING C
(NOW COMPRESSED)

ELECTRO MAGNET
(NOW ENERGISED)

DIAPHRAGM

INLET
FILTER

WATER
TO
MACHINE

H.20596

PRESSURE
REDUCER
INSERT

D

Energized valve.

Main benefits of such valves.
1. The higher the pressure supplied to it the tighter the valve will close.
2. Cost is relatively low.
3. Very reliable.
4. Simple to change if faulty.
Typical faults to watch for (both vented and condenser machines).
1. As with ordinary house taps, the valve seat may wear and allow a small trickle of water to pass even when de-energised. This will cause the machine to fill when not in use if the taps are left turned on over a long period of time and the machine will over-fill, resulting in a possible flood.
2. The valve, when de-energised, may fail to allow the plunger to return to its normal resting/closed position. This problem will cause severe over-fill and flooding. **Note:** Turning off the machine will not stop the over filling in such cases. Complete isolation of both power and water supply is required and, as with step 1, complete renewal will be necessary.
3. The valve fails to allow water to flow due to open circuit in coil winding. See Electrical fault finding (Using a meter) chapter.
4. The valve fails to allow water to flow due to a blocked filter on its inlet. Carefully remove and clean. Do not allow any particle, no matter how small to escape past the filter as it could block the bleed hole.

Water valves come in many sizes and an assortment of shapes, from single valves, double valves and triple valves or a combination of all three. On the double and triple valves, each solenoid operates one outlet from a common inlet. Unfortunately, a fault on one coil or one outlet will generally mean a complete renewal of the whole valve assembly, as individual spare parts are not available. **Note:** On condenser machines with double or triple valves, a restrictor will be fitted to one of the valve outlets. It is important that any replacement valve has this internal restrictor

Single valve: Red for hot supply. White for cold supply.

Double valves 90 degrees and 180 degrees outlet respectively. Typical use would be one side for wash/rinse cycles, the other for restricted condenser supply.

Triple valve configuration typical use would be pre-wash. Main wash and restricted condenser supply.

With the filter removed, carefully clean and inspect it (if damaged or if you suspect that dirt may have entered the valve, renew the unit). This procedure can be carried out without removing the valve(s) from the machine. Here, it is shown removed for photographic purposes only.

Double valve clearly showing restrictor in left-hand outlet used for condenser unit supply.

Cleaning of the valve inlet filter can be carried out by carefully removing the filter with pliers. Ensure the filter is not damaged and that no debris gets passed during removal.

fitted. The valve with the restrictor is for water supply to the condenser unit, as it requires a slow trickle of water to operate correctly. See: Drying components chapter, faults confined to condenser machines only.

The condenser washerdrier machines and some condenser dry-only machines appear to be somewhat unusual in that they require a cold water supply during the dry cycle. However, without this water supply, the machine will not dry. The flow of water from the valve during the drying sequence is restricted to slow it to around .35 litres per minute. Restriction of the water flow is by means of a plastic insert in either the valve outlet to the condenser or at the receiving end within the condenser unit itself. The restrictor is simply a plastic insert with small holes through which the water can pass at a given rate. If the restrictor gets blocked for any reason, the water flow will become too slow for the condensing action to take place. Blocking of the

small holes in the restrictor is not uncommon, especially in machines having restrictors or spray points mounted in the condenser unit. Such problems are often related to water hardness. If the restrictor is removed, cracked or moves out of position, the flow of water could become too great thus preventing drying. This would be as a result of a water build up within the machine between the periodic pump action or water droplets being picked up by the air flow and deposited on the clothes.

As the machine uses a separate valve, i.e. one for normal cold inlet for pre-wash, wash and rinsing, and the other restricted for dry cycle only, the machine may fill correctly for wash cycles, but fail to dry when this option is selected if

With the rear penal removed from this Hotpoint combined condenser machine, the single hot valve, top left, and triple cold valve, below it, can clearly be seen. The hose configuration from the valves to both detergent dispenser and conditioner unit (on the right) are clearly visible.

the fault lies within the restricted valve used to supply the condenser unit. When obtaining replacement valves, make sure that if the original valve had a restrictor, the new one must also have a corresponding restrictor fitted to the correct outlet. In common with all valves and hose connections, make sure that they are a secure and water tight fit.

This is especially so with machines that are fitted with restrictors at or within the condenser as pressure can build up within the supply hose (valve to condenser unit) and if not securely fitted, may blow off or weep.

Further details of the condenser unit, its components and specific fault guide can be found in the Drying Components chapter.

VERIFY THE SUSPECTED FAULT

In this theoretical instance, the machine was loaded and a programme selected but failed to fill. Moving the timer/control to a pump out position confirmed that power was being supplied and that the door interlock was working. See: Door Switches (interlocks) chapter.

Box 1. Reselect wash programme to confirm that machine was originally set and turned on correctly.

With the machine correctly set, Box 2 confirms that, although the machine has electrical feed, no water is entering to begin the filling/washing action.

Box 3. This may seem too obvious to mention, but many an engineer has been called out to find the taps were in the off position. This normally brings the comment that the taps are 'never turned off', and in this case it must have been some other devious member of the family or innocent plumber that has done the dirty deed! This

comment brings in the cardinal rule that all automatic washing machines and dishwashers should be turned off at their isolation taps when the machine is not in use. This may seem a quite pointless task, but the objective is simple. If an inlet pipe should split, or an inlet valve fails to close correctly, a quite disastrous flood could occur. This would not be the case however, if the taps were turned off between each use.

Box 4. By unscrewing the hose from the valve, confirmation of water supply can be easily checked by turning the tap to which it is connected, on and off, ensuring that the free end of the hose is held in a suitable container. Failure of water flow could be due to a faulty tap or tap shaft or an internal fault of the supply hose. Some makers of machines supply rubber inlet hose seals which have a metal or gauze filter moulded into them. It is recommended in the manufacturer's instruction booklet, that the two washers supplied with the filters are fitted at the isolation tap end of the supply hose as a first line filter for the valves. Check if such filter washers were used during the original installation by unscrewing the supply hose from the isolation tap. Clean or renew as required.

Box 5. The checking of the water valve inlet filter can be carried out while the hose is removed for Step 4. Take care not to allow any particles to escape past the fine mesh filter and into the valve. Carefully clean the filter of all scale and debris, etc., and refit. **Note:** The filter can be removed by gently gripping the centre with pliers and pulling it free of the main valve body.

Box 6. Ensure that the water supply to the valve is adequate to operate the valve. See: Basics – plumbing chapter.

Box 7 & 8. If the heater is found to be on when there is no water in the machine, a pressure system fault is indicated and should be checked. Details of this process will be found in the Water level control (Pressure system) chapter. If the heater is in the off position when there is no water in the machine, the valve would appear to be suspect. The valve is easily changed by removing the fixing screws and detaching the internal hose/s from the valve. Making a note of the wiring and hose connections that are on the valve, remove them and replace with a new valve assembly by simply reconnecting the hoses and wires in a reverse sequence.

Chapter 18

Water level control

This Zanussi machine has a rigid pressure vessel (left-hand side of picture) connected to the sump hose.

Modern automatic washing and combined washerdrier machines will have several fill levels each of which corresponds to the type of wash cycle selected, e.g. high level fill for delicate programmes and lower level for the more robust wash programmes. There may also be the facility for an intermediate level option if a half load selection is available to the programme. The way in which the amount of water used for a selected programme is governed by a pressure system.

pressure hoses that function in the same way as the rigid pressure vessel. These hoses will either be grommet fitted to the lower part of the outer tub, or directly moulded to the sump hose. Machines that have moulded plastic outer tubs normally have provision for a rigid pressure vessel to be mounted on the lower section. Although the position and style of the switch and pressure vessels vary, the basic way in which they operate does not.

WHAT IS A PRESSURE SYSTEM?

The pressure system governs the level of water in the machine.

WHERE IS IT LOCATED?

The pressure switch has no standard fixture location, but is usually to be found at the top of the machine. It can be identified as the large circular switch that has several wires and a plastic or rubber tube attached to it leading to a pressure vessel. Several variations of pressure vessel are available. It may be an integral part of the plastic filter housing located behind the front face of the machine's shell, alternatively it may be an independent unit located to the rear or front of the outer tub. There are also

Photograph showing the position of the pressure switch in a typical automatic. The positions may vary with makes, but all will be found as high in the machine as possible.

Typical triple level switch, which is more common on machines with plastic tubs or plastic drum paddles.

Showing the pressure vessel used on machines such as Hoover, Creda and Servis.

HOW DOES IT WORK?

The pressure switch does not actually come into contact with water, but uses air pressure trapped within the pressure vessel or pressure hose. When water enters the tub and the level rises, it traps a given amount of air in the pressure vessel. As the water in the tub rises, this increases the pressure of the trapped air within the pressure vessel. This pressure is then transferred to a pressure sensitive switch via the small bore flexible tube.

A typical pressure system.

The pressure switch is a large circular device that houses a thin rubber diaphragm, which is expanded by the corresponding pressure exerted on it. The diaphragm rests alongside a bank of up to three switches, each of which is set to operate at a different level of pressure. Operating in this way the switch is totally isolated from the water ensuring maximum safety.

POSSIBLE FAULTS IN THE PRESSURE SYSTEM

To create the highest pressure in the chamber of the pressure vessel, the vessel must be positioned as low as possible in the machine. Unfortunately, any sediment that forms in the machine is liable to collect at this point and can therefore easily block the entrance to the vessel. Similarly, because of its very small internal diameter, the pressure tube can also block. The pressure that this device creates is very small, and can easily be blocked by a very small obstruction, such as a lump of powder or sediment deposits.

Typical double level switch.

Single level switch.

Any loose connections on the pressure system will allow the pressure to drop. This will cause overfilling. Ensure a good seal.

Check the pressure tube for chafing and small porous cracks. Renew if suspect.

An internal view of a pressure switch, showing the diaphragm and switches. This pressure switch was faulty due to a small hole appearing in the internal diaphragm. Operation would appear correct, although the pressure would decrease during the wash, and the machine would overfill. If the first functional test was rushed, this type of fault could be overlooked. The switch in the picture, was stripped down to confirm the fault only. These switches require replacement when faulty, as they cannot be repaired.

The seals and hoses of the system are also of great importance. These should be checked for air leaks and blockages. Any puncture or blockage would create a loss of pressure, resulting in the incorrect operation of the switches, i.e. if the air pressure in the pressure vessel were to leak out, the vessel would fill with water. Indicating that the machine was in fact empty, the water valves would be re-energised, thus filling an already full machine. The results would be obvious.

The above example assumed that the air was prevented from actuating the pressure switch. If a blockage occurred whilst the switch was pressurised, the machine would work as normal until the machine emptied. The next time a programme was started the pressure switch would already be pressurised. Therefore the machine would not take any water, but proceed to turn the heater on. Although most heaters are now fitted with a T.O.C. (thermal overload cut-out – see Jargon), this may not act until some damage has been done to the clothes inside the drum.

Points to note
(a) The pressure system should be checked at yearly or half yearly intervals, depending on the water hardness in your area.
(b) Any hoses or tubes that have been disturbed must be resealed, and any clips tightened.
(c) Blowing down the accessible end of the pressure tube may seem an easy solution to remove a blockage, but this may only be a temporary cure. Also, water may enter the pressure vessel before you can push the end of the tube back onto the pressure switch. This will render the pressure system inaccurate, if not useless.
(d) The use of a quality low lather detergent specifically

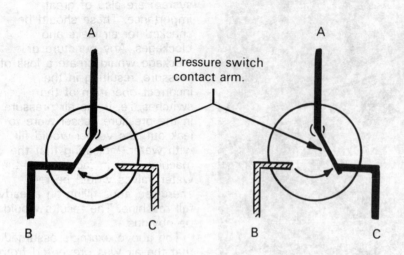

Pressure switch contact arm.

Diagrams illustrate the theoretical operation of a single level pressure switch. A. Being the live supply. Point B is the empty position of the pressure switch, and in this position power supplied to A via the programme timer would be allowed to flow to the fill valve via B. When the preset level of water is reached, the diaphragm if the pressure switch pushes the contact arm across to contact C. Power to the fill valve is therefore stopped and transferred to connection C, which in turn could supply the circulation motor and heater, for instance.

Position when machine has reached level A.C.

Contact arm

Rubber diaphragm

Inlet from pressure vessel.

formulated for use in automatic machines is essential. Failure to use the correct detergent will result in foam entering the pressure system and rendering it, at best, inaccurate.

A pressure switch should only be suspected when the system has been thoroughly cleaned, checked, sealed and re-tested.

CHECKING A PRESSURE SWITCH

Blowing into the switch via the pressure tube, the audible 'clicks' of the switches should be heard. This should also happen when the pressure is released. If your machine uses a single level of water, one click will be heard. Two levels of water will produce two clicks. If your machine has an economy button, a third faint click will also be heard. **Note:** Do not blow too hard as this may damage the switch. Remember the pressure they operate on is very low.

Many machines have an over-fill level detection system which will activate the outlet pump should any excess water enter the machine for any reason. Several systems use the third or fourth switch of the existing pressure switch bank, operated

The Figure below illustrates the way a 3 level switch is used in conjunction with an economy switch, to give an alternative level as an economy feature.

Economy Switch
(½ Load Button)

Triple Level Switch

Fig. 4   B   C   E   D

only by the increased pressure caused by the over-fill.

Unfortunately, systems that use the same pressure vessel for both normal and abnormal water level detection may fail to detect over-filling if it is caused by a blocked pressure vessel or hose fault that allows the pressure to escape.

Systems using a separate pressure vessel and a separate pressure switch for detecting over-filling are much less prone to failures of this nature. Nevertheless, they still require cleaning and checking frequently.

Main faults within the pressure switch
(a) When the diaphragm becomes 'holed' or porous. The switch can be operated and clicks heard, but will click back again without being de-pressurised.
(b) The contact points inside the switch may 'weld' themselves together which would not be uncommon if an item such as a heater were to short circuit and blow a fuse. This would alter the number of clicks heard, as one or more switches may be inoperative. Movement of the unit can often free the contact

points, although this will not be a lasting repair, as the switch will inevitably fail again due to contact point damage.

Any of the above faults require the fitting of a new switch. The make, model and serial number of the machine should be stated when ordering, as pressure switches are internally pre-set for specific machines, although the external appearance is similar. Fitting is a simple direct exchange between the old and new.

The diagram illustrates the operation of a double level pressure switch. Fig. 1 shows the machine filling with water. If B and E are taken as hot and cold valves respectively, it can be seen that the machine is filling with both of the valves. In Fig. 2 the lowest level of water is reached. The pressure breaks the connection with the hot valve (B), and remakes it with the heater switch (C). The cold valve (E) continues filling. Fig. 3 shows the highest level, with the cold fill stopping, switching in the motor (D).

Fig. 4 illustrates the way a three-level switch is used in conjunction with an economy switch, to give an alternative level as an economy feature.

FIG 1   FIG 2   FIG 3

B   C   D   E | B   C   D   E | B   C   D   E

The diagram above illustrates the theoretical operation of a double level pressure switch. Fig. 1 shows the machine filling with water. If B and E are taken as hot and cold valves respectively, it can be seen that the machine is filling with both hot and cold water. In Fig. 2 the lowest level of water is reached. The pressure breaks the connection with the hot valve (B), and remakes it with the heater switch (C). The cold valve (E) continues filling. Fig. 3. shown the highest level, with the cold fill stopping, switching in the motor (D).

CLEARING A PRESSURE SYSTEM BLOCKAGE

1. Note and remove all connections to the pressure switch. Remove complete system from machine.

2. Check connecting hose for blockages at both ends and blow down tube to check for air leaks and to clear it if any obstructions.

3. Clean inlet to pressure vessel and check hose for leaks and/or perishing.

4. Carefully check outlet of pressure vessel for any build up of sludge.

5. Wash out pressure vessel thoroughly to remove any loose particles and sludge.

When refitting check the pressure tube and any rubber hose connections for wear (i.e., rubbing on pulley, belt or clips).

A similar procedure should be followed for all types of pressure vessel and care should be taken to re-seal all hose connections that are removed. Remember to wash clear all loose particles, etc., as even the smallest of blockages in this system will cause trouble.

PRESSURE VESSEL VARIATIONS

A grommet fit pressure hose.

A front fitting pressure vessel of the type used for Hotpoint machines.

Pressure hose fitting on the under side of the outer tub. The grommet fitting to the tub can leak, so ensure that the good seal is maintained should the hose be removed for cleaning.

Chapter 19

Pumps

The pump is a vital part of the correct functioning of the machine and prone to various faults. Leaks from the pump may not be apparent, but the resulting pool of water usually is. So here are a few points to look out for.

Firstly check all clips on the hoses to and from the pump and tighten if they are loose.

If the leak remains, the pump's shaft seal should be checked. This is the seal that forms a water-tight barrier on the rotating shaft of the motor directly between the impeller, and the front motor bearing. The seal can be broken by a collection of fluff/lint forming between the seal and the impeller itself, thus distorting the rubber seal. To check if this is happening, remove the pump chamber, by removing its securing clips or screws, and whilst securing the rotor of the pump motor, turn the impeller clockwise to undo it from the shaft, (impeller and rotor are often left-hand threaded). Having done this, remove any objects adhering to the shaft and refit, ensuring the pump chamber seal is in position. If the seal still leaks, it will be because it is worn or the seal has softened. On most machines, this means the complete renewal of the pump, not as costly as you may think, as many genuine and 'patterned' pumps of good quality are now available at very low cost. This may seem drastic for such a small seal, but the fact that water containing detergent would have been entering the front pump bearing, long before the leak was bad enough to see, means the pump will probably be damaged itself and next in line to cause trouble.

The only pump where complete renewal can be avoided is the early Hoover type, with a large flat disc-like seal, which is the pump chamber seal, and the shaft seal in one. If the seal has leaked, the front bearing should be replaced at the same time as the seal. If the rotor shaft was found to be worn, (even slightly, i.e. roughness/scoured), it would probably be easier and quicker to fit a complete compatible pump, to avoid any further trouble. In fact this could be the least expensive remedy.

Other leaks can be attributable to the pump, due for example to impeller damage, that is to say blades of impeller broken off or badly worn away by a solid object lodged in the pump at sometime, e.g. small coin or tight bearings causing slow running of motor.

Both of the above will result in poor water discharge, i.e. slow draining which can be detected by functional testing. This in turn may cause the machine to spin whilst some water still remains, thus causing other hoses, etc., on the machine to leak or the machine to fill to too high a level, as some machines have a timed rinse fill action. On other machines slow drainage may mean that the machine does not spin at all. This is due to the pressure switch detecting the presence of water in the machine which the slow pump failed to discharge in its allotted time, therefore not allowing a spin to take place by either missing out the spin completely or stopping the wash cycle at the spin positions. This may occur on the intermediate spin half way through the rinse sequence on many machines.

Checking the impeller and bearings can be done at the same time as checking the seal.

Similar faults on condenser drying machines may give rise to poor drying due to the failure to discharge the condensate and water used/produced in the drying process quickly enough. This leads to a build-up within the outer tub which is sufficient enough to wet the clothes but not high enough to be visible. Ensure the correct pump out rate by using a functional test sequence. the pump on a condenser machine is operated periodically or continuously (depending on make and model) during the drying sequence to discharge the condensate and water. Failure due to wear is more common on condenser washerdrier machines although some manufacturers do fit more robust pumps to compensate for this. Always fit the correct replacement pump and make sure it has a T.O.C. To avoid premature failure, a good quality pump must be fitted and the machine should be serviced regularly.

Shown is a simple illustration of the outlet pump chamber and impeller. Water from the sump enters from the front. The rotation of the impeller lifts the water in the direction of the narrower outlet hose. Some machines are fitted with a non-returnable valve system on the outlet hose, watch out for blockages at this point. There are two types of impeller. One is simply a paddle type and more prone to blockages, the other type is like the one illustrated and is called a vortex pump. This type of impeller is more of a flat etched disc that allows a gap between itself and the pump chamber. This gap lets particles pass through easier

than the bladed impeller version. The vortex impeller applies lift to the water as shown in the diagram on the left. The action is similar to the rotating vortex created when a bath or sink empties.

TYPICAL PUMP REPLACEMENT

Note: Ensure that the machine is isolated before attempting any

repair on your washing machine. The following sequence of pictures shows the location of the pump assembly on a Hoover automatic, the position of which is almost standard throughout the entire Hoover range of both wash only and combined machines.

The machine was leaking badly when inspected, but was in fact still working. When questioned the user admitted that the machine had been leaking for some considerable time, but now more water seemed to be leaking out than ever before. As you may see, this is obvious in pictures 3 & 4, by the degree of corrosion to both pump and the shell of the machine. (This level of corrosion would have been avoided by earlier detection/report of the initial much smaller leak.)

Shown in pictures 5 & 6 are variations of pumps that may be encountered on this type of machine. Pictures 7 to 12 show the further stripdown of the pump. In this case, it was

Vortex style pump. Dynamic force exerted on the water in the direction of the outlet.

Access to typical sump hose filter or catch pot. As can be seen from photographs A and B, pump positions vary between makes but the basic operation is the same.

B. Pump mounted right-hand side directly to sump hose with internal filter only accessible during routine servicing.

thought best to renew the pump completely because of the amount of water and detergent damage to both the bearings and metal laminations of the stator. Again, this could have been avoided if the earlier leak had been dealt with sooner.

The complete pump of the type shown in picture 6 was fitted, and the shell and mounts were coated with anti-rust compound prior to the fitting of the pump. Care must be taken that the anti-corrosion liquid does not come into contact with any rubber hoses or seals.

After replacing all hoses and connections, (a simple reversal of the removal procedure) the machine was moved back into its correct working position and re-connected to the water and power supply. All connections and work was double checked

A. Pump mounted lower left-hand side Phillips washerdrier connected to accessible front filter unit.

This new type of pump uses a permanent magnet rotor and avoids many of the problems associated with early pumps. It is becoming popular with many manufacturers. A description of how the motor works is given in the Motors chapter.

Typical electric pump with sump hose and outlet hose of the type found on many of the leading makes. The main differences with electric pumps are the pump chamber mouldings. All pumps, empty at about 8 gallons per minute.

1. Ensure that machine is isolated and remove rear panel. Note location of pump – back, right-hand corner.

prior to a short rinse programme being selected to ensure that the new pump functioned correctly, that the re-positioned clips were watertight and that no other leaks were present, prior to a full functional test via an R.C.D. protected supply.

At this point, the user was advised of the unnecessary danger (and damage in this case) caused by using the machine whilst ignoring a very obvious fault.

Note: In most modern machines, wash-only and washerdriers, the pump has to be changed as a complete unit for even the smallest of problems.

The anti-corrosion coat mentioned can be one of several types available from D.I.Y. car centres and hardware shops. Use it as per the manufacturer's instructions only, taking care not to allow any contact with rubber hoses or plastics. When using anti-corrosion gel or rubber sealant indoors, care should be taken to protect the floor from spillage, and ensure that adequate ventilation is available.

2. Machine face protected and carefully laid over. Position of pump now clearly visible.

3. Note and remove the hose clips and connections. Corrosion may be found on the mounting. At this point treat with anti-rust compound prior to refitting.

4. Support pump whilst removing securing bolts and withdraw pump from machine.

5. Shown are two types of Hoover pump that may be found. (Different styles of impeller and stator).

8. Note pump chamber position and remove to expose impeller.

10. Rear seal exposed. In this case it is badly worn by a build up of lint upon shaft.

6. This type of pattern pump will fit Hoover, Creda, Servis and Hotpoint. Many other styles are available for other machines.

11. Seal removed and front bearing checked for wear and damage. Also check rear bearing.

7. Lever small clips loose using small bladed screwdriver. Hold clip lightly to prevent it springing off. Screws may be found in place of clips.

9. Whilst holding rear shaft securely, turn impeller clockwise and remove. (LH thread).

12. Rear view of seal showing extensive wear.

13. When fitting a new pump as in this instance, check the bolt hole sizes of the mounting plate. On some occasions they may need enlarging.

14. Secure pump firmly into position.

15. Reconnect the terminals. If the pump has an earth tag, ensure that it is a good fit, as with all connections.

16. If a pump has a plastic mounting plate, it is essential that the metal stator laminations are linked to the machine earth path. Make a short lead to connect the earth tag on the pump to the fixing bolt and secure firmly. When the hoses and clips have been re-fitted, the machine is ready for testing on the rinse cycle. Ensure all panels are refitted before commencing functional testing.

Chapter 20

Door switches (interlocks)

WHAT IS AN INTERLOCK?

The name interlock is given to an electrical switch behind or near the main door latching device of washing machines and is designed to give a time delay of up to two minutes, before the door can be opened. The delay time differs between the makes and models of different machines.

WHAT ARE THE DIFFERENT TYPES?

A machine with a push/pull timer knob action, may also have a manual interlock thus giving double protection. The manual interlock system is quite straightforward, bolting or unbolting the door with a push/pull action of the timer knob, via a latching mechanism. The mechanical interlock acts in much the same way as the electrical version in preventing entry via the door if the machine is turned on except that there is no time delay. Such mechanical interlocks are always in addition to electrical interlocks which incorporate a delay to entry.

A more recent version of interlock also incorporates a

pressure switch type of system, that will not allow the door to open if there is any water remaining in the machine. This again is a mechanical operation and will work even when the machine is unplugged. The door can only be opened when the water has been drained out. This must be remembered in the case of a pump failure or blockage. The system is easily recognisable by the pressure tube leading to the door interlock. Such systems may use a separate pressure vessel or a 'T' junction arrangement from the water level pressure switch tube. Whichever system is used, faults similar to those described in the water level control section will be encountered, e.g. blockages, air leaks, etc.

Some washerdrier machines may also include a simple microswitch attached to the door interlock forming one unit. The microswitch is in circuit during the dry cycle and

New style interlock with pressure lock included. This works in conjunction with the pressure switch, and does not allow the door to open if any water remains in the machine.

Zanussi 3DB style interlock.

operates directly via the door latch and slide action of the interlock. Such microswitches and interlock combinations are used on machines when the two minute delay facility during

Washerdrier interlock with integral microswitch to rear. Note how access was gained via door seal front lip by removal of front clamp band. See Door Seal chapter.

Typical dry only door safety switches. Note the operating arms. As the switch carries all the power it is liable to overheating problems due to poor connections or contacts.

Internal view of interlock which uses the oil-filled piston arrangement in place of a bi-metal strip. The piston can be seen in the lower section of the interlock running through its large return spring on the left and supported on the right by the heater pod.

the dry cycle is not used. This arrangement allows the door to be opened if required, but the microswitch would open circuit and interrupt the cycle. **Note:** Great care must be exercised with combined washerdriers as the door glass can reach extremely high temperatures. Take care to keep children out of reach when the machine is in use. Adults should also be made aware of such dangers. On basic tumble dry only machines, a simple microswitch actuated by the door latch pecker or hinge movement is used. No delay action is available and simply opening and closing the door stops and restarts the programme. Details of this system is given later in this section.

Solenoid operated interlock as used on many computer controlled machines. The microswitch is clearly visible as is the cord for manual actuation of the interlock in the event of power failure/fault.

The 'Rold' interlock is becoming increasingly popular with today's manufacturers. Shown is the Fagor variant. Also found in Indesit machines.

Double pressure switch system with 'T' junction and tube to the right leading down to a pressure operated interlock.

A typical microswitch from the tumble dry only machine. The switch is a simple ON/OFF function with no delay or locking action.

Diagram A. shows the state of the interlock before power at L. It can be seen that the door bolt is disengaged and the bi-metal strip is in its 'rest' position. Because of this, there is no connection at point Y. Therefore no power is transmitted to X.

Diagram B. shows the state of the interlock when power is applied to point L. The heater is activated, therefore heating the bi-metal strip. This then bends, engaging the door bolt and making the connection at Y, allowing power to flow to X. When the power is

HOW DOES A BASIC INTERLOCK WORK?

Because manufacturers prefer to have their own version of interlock, it is impossible to illustrate all of the different types. Because of this, the Klixon (3DB) type of switch is used to illustrate the internal workings and theory.

Schematic wiring diagram of a simple tumble dry only machine.

Interlock 3DB Operation

Diagram (A) shows the start of the interlock before power at (L). It can be seen that the door bolt is disengaged and the bi-metal strip is in its 'rest' position. Because of this, there is no connection at point (Y), therefore no power is transmitted to (X).

Diagram (B) shows the state of the interlock when power is applied to point (L). The heater is activated, therefore heating the bi-metal strip. This then bends, engaging the door bolt and making the connection at (Y). This then allows power to flow to (X).

disconnected, the heater is allowed to cool and the bi-metal strip then bends back to its rest position. This action can take up to two minutes, thus creating the delay. The delay time (cooling of heater and bi-metal) will vary according to the ambient temperature, style of interlock and position of the appliance. Some makes and variations of interlocks use a small oil filled piston arrangement in place of the bi-metal strip. When heated, the oil expands and the resulting piston movement is used to actuate the interlock. As with the bi-metal system described, cooling allows the piston to retract and de-latch the interlock. **Note**: The heater referred to in this part of the manual is not the large heater in the drum, but is of minute proportions and is only used to heat the bi-metal strip.

Modern machines tend to link the interlock to all of the other functions of the machines, so if

the interlock should fail, power to the rest of the machine would be severed and the machine would then be totally inoperable. With older machines, interlock failure would only result in no motor action throughout a normal programme.

A two tag interlock (1DB) is called a straight through interlock as, although locking occurs, switching does not.

INTERLOCKS (COMPUTER CONTROLLED)

Computer-controlled machines (as opposed to mechanically controlled) may have similar electro-mechanical interlocks to those described in the previous paragraphs. Alternatively, depending on make and model, they could be completely different both in the way the

door is opened and the way that access is restricted via the door until the programme has finished and the machine is completely empty of water. A breakdown of basic operation is as follows though it does not typify any specific make as manufacturers will incorporate subtle differences to create individuality of product.

Door opening is by means of a push button action that actuates a simple electrical switch which then makes contact and supplies power to a solenoid operated catch mounted within the machine in place of the door interlock. With power supplied to the solenoid in this way the door latch is released and the door opens. To avoid continuous supply to the solenoid, a micro-switch is incorporated within the unit to open circuit the solenoid coil as soon as the door latch pecker is released. The opening operation of the door depends on:

1. Power being supplied to the machine and the machine being turned on.
2. No programme is currently operating.
3. No motor action or drum rotation is taking place.
4. Any water in the machine is below the lowest detectable level of the pressure switch, i.e. all switches in rest position.
5. Door open button is pressed.

The requirements of steps 2-5 are monitored continuously by the micro-processor within the electronically-controlled timer. With condition 1, a power supply is necessary for the door solenoid to operate. However, in power failure or fault situations, many machines have means of de-latching the door mechanism manually; reference should be made to the appliance handbook for further information. Before carrying out mechanical actuation of the latch, ensure the machine is unplugged (isolated) and that the water level is below the door level, see: Emergency procedures chapter and photo in this section.

Several machines use an LED (light emitting diode) or display to indicate when door opening can be activated.

The use of a micro-processor within such machines allows for greater interaction and sensing to be carried out. Due to the larger memory size of the chips used, more variable programming is possible. The way in which the programme is written enables it to react to variations within the circuit of the machine which in turn gives rise to a greater number of criteria being monitored to ensure compliance with safety, etc. The micro-processor board also includes a clock chip which can help in controlling programme times and functions accurately. The timing function can also be used to time a delay to the door open switch if required by the manufacturer of the machine.

TUMBLE DRY ONLY MACHINE

Most tumble dry only machines do not incorporate a time delay system and access to the load compartment is therefore not restricted by time. There will be, however a micro-switch actuated when the door is opened which will to open circuit and sever power to the motor to stop drum rotation. As the rotation is slow on dry-only machines the drum will quickly stop when the motor is turned off by the micro-switch. On some machines, only the motor is open circuited by the opening of the door, leaving the heater still in circuit. The motor used to rotate the drum usually rotates the fan which circulates the air, therefore in such machines, if only the motor is stopped when the door is opened, the heater temperature will quickly rise and open circuit its T.O.C. If the door is left open for long periods, cycling of the T.O.C. will occur with the possibility of damage to both T.O.C. and heater. **Note**: This will only occur if the timer is still on the heat section and will

only cycle until the remaining heat time runs out, i.e. completes its preset time. Continuous opening and closing the door is not recommended. To avoid such problems many machines now use the door micro-switch to open circuit supply to all components. Make yourself aware of the system used in your machine.

Computer-controlled tumble dry only machines use a system similar to that described in the previous section. Dry programmes on such machines, once interrupted will not restart by simply closing the door but require the re-pressing of the start button.

Similar systems can be found on the higher specification mechanically-timed machines. These machines use a relay start once normal operation has been interrupted, i.e. by door opening. The remaining portion of the drying time cannot commence until the start button is pressed. This type of system is much safer than the simple micro-switch only operation which will restart the drum rotating as soon as the door is closed.

Chapter 21

Heaters

Overheated terminal due to loose connection on live supply.

Heating elements come in a variety of shapes and sizes, but the elements used in washerdriers and tumbledriers are usually one of two basic types: 1. exposed single wire elements used exclusively in dry-only machines, and 2. metal sheathed elements found in washerdriers, for heating the air flow (mounted in a special duct on combined washerdriers) and for heating the wash water (immersion type). The solid/sheathed element is also used in many dry-only machines to heat the air flow.

The former type is simply an exposed length of conductor which heats up when a current is passed through it owing to the resistance properties of wire. Being an exposed conductor means that it must be housed and supported in such a way as to avoid accidental contact which could cause electric shock or burns. It must also be housed in such a way that it can dissipate the heat generated and be supported by heat resistant insulators at regular intervals.

SHEATHED ELEMENTS

Metal covered (shrouded) elements can be found in all three types of machines, vented washerdrier, condenser washerdrier and dry-only. The way in which it is insulated and supported by its solid outer sheath allows it to be bent and shaped into any one of thousands of configurations to suit any situation. This however, can only be done at manufacture and no modification or bending should be done to old or new elements.

The way in which they work is the same as written previously, when a current is passed along the conductor its resistance gives rise to heating of the conductor. However, the conductor in this type of element is housed within a tube and surrounded by an insulating material (magnesium oxide). Heat can be transferred to the outer sheath, but the current cannot. Outer sheaths are made from various types of metal to suit the particular requirements and conditions. Some are for use with the heating portion of the element submerged in water, whereas others are used within the machine to heat the air flow during the drying cycle.

The design of both exposed and sheathed elements vary enormously from product to product, but the way in which they work remains the same. As with motors, a T.O.C. is normally present to avoid overheating. The T.O.C. is a common area of fault and replacements must be identical to the original. To avoid overheating, make sure of a good air flow over the element, i.e. check that fluff, etc., does not block the air intake.

One variation of exposed element used in many tumble dry only machines.

Wash water heater is clearly visible on the lower right-hand side of the outer tub backhalf of this condenser washerdrier machine.

Sheathed airflow heaters are used in combined machines. Shown are Newpol type.

TEMPERATURE CONTROL

There are several ways in which the temperature is controlled, details of which can be found in the following chapter on temperature control.

MAIN FAULTS WITH HEATERS

One of the most common faults with heaters, both exposed and sheathed versions is that of open circuit, i.e. no current flows through the heater, therefore no heat is produced. This can simply be due to a broken or

Heater duct of a Philips washerdrier machine (condenser type).

loose connection to one of the heater terminals. This then overheats, leaving an obvious discoloration of the connection or terminal, resulting in a break of the circuit at that point. Alternatively, the break in the circuit can occur within the element itself. Heaters can easily be tested for continuity as described in the Using a Meter chapter.

Another fault that can occur is that of low insulation. In this case, please refer to the chapter on Low Insulation. Accompanying the low insulation fault is that of short circuiting of the heater caused by either a complete breakdown

Typical configuration of airflow heaters housed in the ducting of a combined machine.

of insulation of sheathed elements or the breaking of exposed elements/mounts allowing the exposed element to touch the earthed metal heat shield or housing. This results in the appliance blowing fuses or earth tripping if an R.C.D. is in circuit.

Should any of the above faults occur, a complete replacement of the component(s) is required. **Note:** Broken exposed style elements that touch an earthed metal heat shield will only blow wired fuses if the remaining element circuit is short and resistance low. It is possible for the remaining length of element to work using the earth as its neutral return. This type of fault results in poor drying through the reduced size and heat output of element. Check exposed elements and their mounts closely for this type of problem. If this fault does occur on an R.C.D. protected circuit, i.e. household supply or via adaptor type during functional test, etc., the R.C.D. would trip preventing further use of the machine until the fault is rectified.

WHERE IS THE WASH WATER HEATER LOCATED?

The wash water heater is usually located in the lower part of the tub assembly, and can be either fitted through the back half of the tub or through an aperture in the tub base itself. One exception to this is the Hotpoint front loader range, including combined machines, where the heater is located on the front of the outer tub, directly below the door seal. Access is gained by removing the front panel of the machine. Details of this are to be found in the Door Seal chapter.

REMOVAL AND REFITTING OF A HEATER

After making a note of the connections and removing them, the heater can be withdrawn from its position by slackening, but not removing the centre nut, and tapping it to release the tension then gently easing the

rubber grommet free from its position with a large flat-bladed screwdriver. Refitting is a reversal of these instructions, although a little sealant should be applied to both surfaces of the grommet fitting. Care should be taken that the centre nut is not overtightened, as this would cause a distortion of the metal plate. On most automatic washing machines, the inner of the outer tub has a raised flange or cover plate that engages the curved section at the end of the heater. It is important that this is located correctly when refitting the heater. Check that it is located and held correctly by pressing firmly but carefully downwards on the terminals of the heater whilst slowly rotating the inner drum. If the heater is not located correctly it will pivot on the grommet mounting and allow the element to come into contact with the drum, resulting in a grating noise and vibration. If such a noise is experienced during this simple test, slacken the heater clamp centre nut, remove the heater completely and relocate it correctly then try again.
Note: Do not exert excessive pressure on the terminals of the heater. Try to press down on the exposed outer sheath.

Machines that have plastic or nylon outer tubs are fitted with overheat protectors. These are essential and are linked in line with the live feed to the heater. They are fitted for safety reasons, for if a pressure switch or pressure system were to fail, it is possible for the heater to be engaged with no water in the tub.

This would be most unwelcome in a machine with a metal tub, although only minor damage would be caused to the clothes. If this type of fault were to happen in a plastic/nylon tub, the result would be extremely dangerous.
Note: Under no circumstances should the overheat protection

Sheathed elements can also be found in tumble dry only machines. They are normally in a large circular single or double configuration as shown. They can be mounted to the front or rear of the machine depending on make and model.

Exposed heater element (spiral type) supported on ceramic mounts (type 1).

Spiral element kit for Hoover tumble dry only machine. Note – new glass fibre support cores. When fitting, measure fixing length required using a piece of string and pre-stretch new element before fitting it to the machine. Keep stretching along the whole length evenly otherwise hot spots will form.

This Zanussi unit displays a typical broken element fault. A complete unit replacement is required in this instance.

With the large rear cover removed from this Philips tumble dry only machine, the heater assembly and fan are easily accessible for cleaning, etc.

This wash water element shows signs of scaling and fluff contamination.

Normal style heater. (Do not fit to plastic tub machines).

device be removed or bypassed.

The overheat protector that is used on early Philips machines was an integral part of the heater and is similar to a capillary thermostat switch. However, on later machines, a simple thermostat is used to open circuit the heater if overheat occurs. On the latest machines the thermostat is connected in the live supply between the door interlock to the pressure switch. If overheat occurs the thermostat goes open circuit and cuts power to all other components apart from the door interlock. Hotpoint use a separate thermal fuse heater protector for boil dry protection of their plastic outer tub machines and this item along the late Philips thermostat are available separately.

If such items are found to be faulty, the result would be failure to heat the wash water or failure to move through the programme. If any type of protector is found to be open circuit, it is essential that the cause is identified and rectified prior to renewal. Thoroughly check the pressure system and switch. For more detailed information on thermal fuses and protection devices see the following chapter.

Heater with overheat detector (arrowed). This is found on machines with plastic outer tubs.

AIRFLOW HEATERS (METAL SHEATHED TYPE)

Sheathed elements of similar construction to the water heaters described previously are found in both washerdrier heating units and tumble dry only machines. Because of the restriction of available space in the combined washerdrier, the elements used in washerdrier heating units are of a compact configuration very similar to their water heating counterparts. On the other hand, dedicated dry-only machines which use solid sheathed elements have much longer (often circular) elements. Due to the similarity in construction, the faults encountered will again be open circuit, low insulation and short circuit. Reference to these relevant sections will be required. Details of the various heating units on both washerdrier machines and dry-only appliances are given elsewhere.

AIRFLOW HEATERS (EXPOSED TYPE)

This type of heating element is used predominantly in tumble dry only machines. As can be seen from the accompanying photographs, they are easily distinguishable from the sheathed type of heater. Although several variations and configurations of exposed element are used, they all fall into two basic categories; 1. Simple spiral (spring like) elements, stretched and supported on ceramic holders either in a large circular configuration or a compact box mount system. 2. Single strand element woven into or onto a ceramic or mica support.

It is essential that whatever type is used, it should be correctly supported, free from fluff build-up and all ceramic or mica supports intact. Check closely for any sagging of the element between the supports as this could lead to short circuit between elements on compact heaters and to shorting to earth on the larger circular heaters. Take care when cleaning or removing any fluff as both the supports and the elements themselves become brittle with use and are easily damaged. As with the sheathed elements described earlier, two elements are usually used to allow a high/low heat selection.

Do not make twisted joints to repair a broken element. A faulty element should always be renewed with any broken, cracked or charred support or insulation. The compact types of heater unit are available only as complete units – details of which can be found in the section on Dry Only Machines. The large spiral elements like the ones shown in the photograph can be renewed individually and details of this procedure will also be found in the Dry-only machines chapter.

On machines with large spiral elements a support cord will be found running through the centre of each element, the purpose of which is to prevent the element from shorting to the metal heat shield in the event of it (the element) stretching or breaking. It is essential that the support cord is intact and correctly positioned in order to support the element if breaking or sagging should occur.

On early machines, the support cord was often made of asbestos, and consequently with use, the cord itself became powdery and broke. Take care if this type of support cord is found during repair or servicing as the dust can be harmful if inhaled. Moisten the work area to reduce dust and dispose of the waste carefully. The support cord used now is of glass fibre which is less prone to deterioration and should be used to replace the old type of asbestos element support.

Chapter 22

Temperature control

Single thermostat.

A thermostat is an automatic device for monitoring temperature. This can be water temperature, the direct heat of the heating element (in which case, acting like a T.O.C. See: Heaters chapter), or airflow temperature of combined or dry-only machines. The thermostat (stat) will either 'make' or 'break' a circuit at a pre-determined temperature. Temperature ratings of fixed thermostats are usually marked around the metal perimeter on the back of the stat and are marked NO or NC., i.e. normally open contact (closing and making a circuit at given temperature) or normally closed (opening at given temperature). Some thermostats can and do contain both variants.

Fixed thermostat of the types used in tumble dry only machines for temperature control and overheat safety (T.O.C.)

Double thermostat.

Variable thermostat showing the switches, capillary tube and pod.

WHERE ARE THEY LOCATED?

Positioning of each thermostat depends on the job it has to do. The wash temperature thermostat is usually located on the back half or underside of the outer tub depending on the make and model of the machine.

Exceptions to this are the Hotpoint and Fagor front loading machines, where the thermostat, heater and pressure vessel are located on the front of the outer tub, directly below the door seal. Access to these components is gained by the removal of the front panel of the machine. Details of this are to be found in the Door Seal fitting chapter.

Thermostats used to control/monitor drying temperatures will be located at a strategic point of the airflow, whereas the thermostats used for overheat protection are located in or near the heater ducting (on combined machines) or heat shields (on dry-only machines).

HOW A FIXED THERMOSTAT WORKS

Diagram A. shows a typical fixed (non-variable) thermostat which can have one, two or three settings.
Diagram B. illustrates how a three position thermostat works. The power enters the switch at X, but cannot proceed as there is no contact. As the temperature rises and each preset temperature is reached, the bi-metal disc set to that temperature bends, making one of the three possible contacts.

REMOVING AND REFITTING A STANDARD TYPE THERMOSTAT

After making a note of the connections on the back, disconnect the wires from the rear of the thermostat. Insert a small screwdriver at point (z), and prise the thermostat away

Diagram (A).

Diagram (B).

AT REST POSITION

50° TEMP REACHED

OVERHEAT
SUPPLY TO HEATER DIRECT
CUT OFF

A typical fixed thermostat.

from its grommet fitting. When refitting, it is advisable to smear a little sealant on the grommet to aid correct fitting and avoid leaks. Refitting is a reversal of the removal process. **Note:** Before the removal or repair of any component from the machine, isolate the machine from the main electrical supply by removing the plug from the wall socket.

The diagram shows an alternative style of fixed thermostat, in this instance a 50°C. (NO) normally open contact and a 85°C. (NC) normally closed contact. The latter is a safety thermostat which operates if overheating should occur within the machine.

The diagrams below illustrate the position of the thermostat at rest. Bi-metal discs are mounted directly behind the metal front cover of the stat and are preset to distort at given temperature (in this instance, 50°C. and 85°C). They are linked to contact switches by push rods. Any corresponding distortions of the discs, either make or break the corresponding contacts as shown.

When removed from the machine, the thermostat's operation can be tested by placing the metal cover in contact with a known heat source, e.g. radiator, hot water, etc., which matches or slightly exceeds the required temperature. Allow a little time for the heat to warm the stat and bi-metal discs. Testing for closing or opening of the thermostat can now be carried out as shown in the Using a meter chapter.

Check temperature with a household thermometer and allow a few degrees either way of the marked temperature on the outer rim of the stat, and remember to check if the stat is normally NO or NC. When cool, check that the stat returns to its normal position as indicated on the rim, i.e. NO or NC.

REMOVING AND REFITTING

Make a note of the position, orientation and connections of the thermostat and then disconnect the wires. Insert a small flat-bladed screwdriver between the inner rubber lip and the metal front plate of the stat and prise the stat from the grommet. Care will be required if sealant has previously been used as this will have glued the stat into position. When refitting, it is advisable to smear a little sealant on the grommet to aid fitting and avoid leaks. Refitting is a reversal of the removal process.

THERMOSTAT FITTING

TO REFIT

Locate the metal lip in the grommet recess (D) and with the aid of a flat- bladed screwdriver ease the outer lip over the metal lip of the stat (C). Sealant will help locate and seal the thermostat into position, (E). Ensure that the thermostat is securely located into the grommet and that the outer lip is not trapped.

Thermostats may also be held in position by metal clips or clamps, and again, make sure of a good seal and check that the clips or clamps do not trap or touch any wires or connectors.

THE VARIABLE THERMOSTAT

How a variable thermostat works. Diagram F shows a pod type thermostat. This is found on machines that have a variable wash temperature control. Diagram G is a schematic diagram of the internal workings. This consists of an oil or gas filled pod which is connected to the switch by a capillary tube. When the oil/gas in the pod is heated it expands within the sealed system and pushes a diaphragm. The diaphragm acts on the switchgear thus 'breaking' one circuit and 'making' the other.

When the oil/gas cools it contracts, pulling the switch in the opposite direction. The switch is then in its original position and the process repeats if necessary.

REMOVING AND REFITTING A POD TYPE THERMOSTAT

The pod which is located at the base of the capillary tube must be eased from its rubber grommet gently, taking care not to unduly kink or pull on the capillary tube itself. **Note:** When fitting or refitting this form of thermostat, the capillary tube must not come into contact with any electrical contacts such as the heater terminals or moving parts such as the main drive belt. When fitted, the tube should be checked along its entire length for any possible contact with these items. Also,

Variable Knob Section

Pod Section

Diagram (F) – Typical pod type thermostat.

Pod

Capillory Tube

Piston

Heater Supply

To timer or Motor etc.

Variable Knob on Outside of Machine

Diagram (G) – Internal workings of pod type thermostat.

Indicated in this condenser washerdrier are (A) the variable temperature wash stat control, (B) dual fixed temperature air duct stat and (C) fixed temperature stat being used as a T.O.C. to open circuit the air duct heater in the event of overheating.

The fixed wash temperature stat (D) and pod for the variable stat (E) are shown in position on the rear of the outer tub.

a coiled section of at least two large turns should be left at a convenient position to absorb the movement of the tub assembly.

TESTING A THERMOSTAT

The standard thermostat can be subjected to a known temperature (e.g. radiator, kettle, etc.) and be checked with a small test meter for continuity. This process is shown in the chapter on Using a meter. The pod thermostat can be tested as above, ensuring that only the pod itself is immersed in water.

Note: Whilst at room temperature, the state of the thermostat should be determined. On pod thermostats, the lowest and highest setting should be selected. During testing, ensure that switch actuates both on rise and fall of temperature, see: Using a Meter chapter.

THERMOSTAT OPERATION FLOWCHART

Using the following flowchart, trace the sequence of events:
1. The machine is turned on.
2. The timer impulses, fills the machine with cold water and turns the heater on.
3-4. The thermostat 'waits' until the heater has heated the water to 40°C.
5-6 When the thermostat closes (i.e. the water has reached 40°C), the timer washes for two minutes. The timer starts the washing action for two minutes. (At this point the heater is still engaged).
7-8 The above operation is repeated, again with the heater engaged. When the two minute wash has ended, the water will be at 45°C due to the extra four minutes heating.
9-11 The timer then moves to the next position, which disengages the heater, and is then ready for the programme to continue as required.

12 For the purpose of this flowchart, the washer will end here as we are only concerned with the operation of the thermostat at this time.
Note: This is only used as an example to illustrate the use of the thermostat, and does not actually represent the way in which a wash is formed. For further information regarding the timer, see the chapter Timers (programmers).

This way of using preset thermostats can give a greater variation in wash temperatures. A combination of preset and variable thermostats is common in order to give protection to the cooler washers, i.e. should the variable thermostat be accidentally left at 90°C. and a delicate wash has been selected, the preset stat would override the variable stat, therefore giving some protection to the wash.

1 — TURN ON MACHINE

2 — FILL MACHINE AND TURN ON HEATER

3 — IS WATER AT 40°C   Yes / No

4 — LEAVE HEATER ON

5 — SEND POWER TO TIMER

6 — TWO MINUTES REACHED?   Yes / No

7 — SEND POWER TO TIMER

8 — TWO MINUTES REACHED?   Yes / No

9 — MOVE TIMER TO NEXT POSITION

10 — TURN OFF HEATER

11 — CONTINUE WITH PROGRAMME

12 — END

WHAT IS A THERMISTOR?

A thermistor is a solid state device used in place of a fixed or variable thermostat. The thermistors particular properties allow them to be used as infinitely variable temperature sensors that have no moving parts. They are also incapable of going out of calibration, i.e. giving incorrect temperature resistance values, but occasionally they can and do go 'open circuit', or connections to and from them may short circuit. Both are faults which will inevitable give rise to temperature sensing problems.

Typical solid state thermistor.

Continuity testing a thermistor with a low voltage battery test meter.

WHERE IS IT LOCATED?

Like all temperature sensing devices, it must come into direct or indirect contact with the substance (air/water) or item that needs monitoring. Its location is therefore similar to the other thermostats but methods of fixings will differ.

HOW DOES IT WORK?

Unlike other temperature control devices the thermistor cannot work alone. It is an electrical resistor, the resistance of which varies in relation to its temperature. There are two ways in which it varies depending on manufacturer, and the requirements of the finished product. Thermistors can be positive or negative temperature co-efficient. In simple terms, this means a positive co- efficient thermistor's resistance increases as its temperature increases and conversely, a negative co-efficient thermistor's resistance decreases as its temperature increases. Thermistors are therefore rated as P.T.C. or N.T.C. respectively. The N.T.C. type of thermistor is the version most often used in temperature sensing circuitry in automatic washing machines, e.g. Hoover, Servis, Hotpoint, etc., a theoretical operation of this is given below. It is essential that only the correct variation of thermistor is used which conforms to the rating requirements of the machine and its circuitry.

The variation in resistance to temperature change forms part of an electronic circuit, the output of which controls the advancement of the selected wash programme, in either mechanically or electronically controlled machines. On electronically controlled machines, i.e. those without mechanical timers, the resistance of the thermistor is monitored

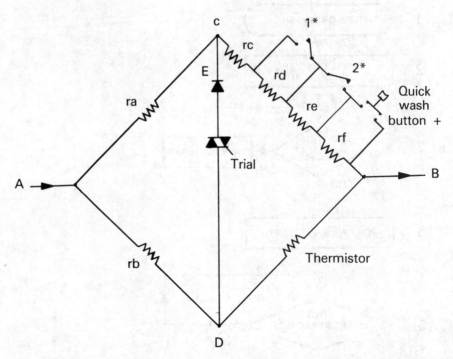

* = Switches controlled by timer wash selection. These switches would be electronic not mechanical on computer controlled machines.
+ = Button on front of machine, i.e. user variation option.

directly by the main programme circuit board or sub-module, see: Timers (programmers). However, thermistors can be found on machines with mechanical timers/programmers and the way in which they work in this instance is as follows. The resistance of the thermistor forms part of a temperature control circuit. There may be a separate module solely for this purpose or it may form part of the motor control module as in some Hotpoint machines. A theoretical operation of such a system is given below.

In this instance the output voltage at D & C are used to control a triac (an electrical component within the circuit). The triac in turn switches the thermostop coil on a mechanical timer or impulse to control panel of a computer control machine. See: Timers (programmers) chapter.

Being an electronic circuit in either mechanical or computer controlled machines, the

operating voltage within this portion of circuit will be low (5 volts DC). Therefore, any electrical testing of the thermistor must be with a low voltage test meter as voltages of over 9 volts will damage the thermistor or module circuitry.

The two resistors Ra and Rb are of the same value. A 5v DC voltage supplied to point A will take one of two routes depending on the resistance opposing it, i.e. A.C.B. or A.D.B. Route A.C.D. has within it four resistors each of which can be switched in and out of the circuit in relation to the programme selected and temperature required for that wash cycle. The diode at point E eliminates reverse supply to the triac. The route A.D.C. contains the thermistor in its second leg D.B. If we assume that the water within the machine is cold, then the thermistor resistance will be high. This will allow a current flow from D. to C. thus energising the thermostop or holding the programme on the heat cycle until the predetermined temperature (governed by the switchable resistors) is attained. Releasing of the thermostop or impulse of programme is as follows. As the water temperature increases, the resistance of the thermistor decreases (N.T.C.). At some point the resistance in both sides of the circuit will be equal and at this point, no current will flow between D. & C. and the triac will switch off. This in turn will release the thermostop on mechanical timers or allow impulse to the next stage of the programme on electronically controlled machines. Variations in temperature are gained by switching in or out the required resistors in the C.B. leg of the circuit, thus altering the point at which equilibrium is reached within the circuit. All switches open = all resistors in circuit RC + RD + RE + RF would result in high resistance, therefore a cooler wash of say 30°C. is achieved. Quick wash switch closed = resistor RF bypassed, i.e. lower total resistance gives wash of say 40°C. Switch 1 closed = two resistors in circuit RC & RE may relate to 50°C with option of quick wash switch to further reduce temperature (and time) if required by user. Switch 2 closed – three resistors RC, RD, RF in circuit may relate to 60°C with option of quick wash switch to further reduce temperature (and time) if required by user. All switches closed = this will leave only RC in circuit at this point, and a high temperature of say 90°C would be achieved, again with option if required.

Note: The option to alter the temperature selected by the set programme, i.e. by pressing a quick wash or short wash option button on the control panel, may be bypassed itself by the timer on some programmes. This means that although in the theoretical operation detailed above, each setting could be further affected by the quick wash switch, in reality, this may not be the case as a quick wash may not be suitable for certain types of wash loads.

T.O.C.s

The term T.O.C. is an abbreviation for thermal overload cut-out. In simple terms, if the item the T.O.C. is attached to or is in proximity with gets too hot (over a predetermined temperature), the T.O.C. will operate and open circuit the supply. The way in which it works is very similar to the thermostat, both of which use the bimetal strip system. Thermostats are in fact used on some machines as T.O.Cs to open circuit for instance the heater if an overheat fault occurs. However, the term T.O.C. generally relates to the smaller devices that are embedded within or on top of motor winding coil of all types, and above the heaters of many makes of tumbledriers.

There are several variations in style and size, each of which being matched to its particular use and position within the appliance or apparatus. It is therefore essential that only the correct style and temperature rating is used when renewing a T.O.C. Those that are used to protect motors, pumps, wash motors, tumbledrier motors, etc., are rarely renewable and usually form part of the original winding or moulding. If a T.O.C. had gone open circuit, it will have done so for a particular reason therefore this safety item must not be bypassed. Always ensure that any replacement component contains a T.O.C. Some pattern spares may miss out this fundamental safety device in order to cut production costs so take note that such an omission could be unsafe.

Although designs and ratings of T.O.C.s vary, there are two basic types of operation.

(a) The self-setting T.O.C. This is like a thermostat and resets when a normal working temperature returns. This may result in a cycling of the fault, i.e. if a tumbledrier outlet or filter is blocked, the heater element will overheat due to a reduced air flow. A safety T.O.C. will open circuit the heater supply. Unfortunately, on all but the most recent machines, when the heater cools, the T.O.C. also cools and in doing so the power would then be returned to the heater and the cycle could then carry on until either the pre-set drying time expired or the element or T.O.C. failed.

(b) The manual reset T.O.C. The action of this type of T.O.C. is identical to that described above except for one main difference. Once tripped, it cannot reset itself and has to be reset manually usually by simply pressing a button or rod.

Note: This must be done with the machine isolated, i.e. unplugged, and only after the cause of the tripping has been eliminated.

Some washerdrier machines incorporate both self-setting T.O.C. for low temperature fault levels but a manual reset if a cycling fault should occur or if the self-setting component should fail (in the closed position). Tripping of both self-setting and manual T.O.C. are common in both washerdriers and tumbledriers if there is a build up of fluff or the air flow is restricted. Filters must always be kept clear and any tripping of the safety devices should be immediately investigated and the cause rectified. A delay of up to four minutes (sometimes more) is possible before manually resetable T.O.C.s can be reset. Modern tumble dryers from 1990 onwards now incorporate a manual reset T.O.C. as standard. Machines that have this facility will have a reset button accessible on the

Two variations of bladed self-resetting T.O.C.s widely used to protect elements in tumble dry only machines from overheat. They are available in a wide range of temperature settings.

Bladed self setting T.O.C. in position between the spiral elements of a Hoover tumble dry only machine (centre of photo).

The button of manual re-set T.O.C. is located on the rear of this tumble dry only machine. Manual re-set T.O.C.s can also be found in some combined machines.

outer casing, the position of which will vary from make to make. Before resetting, ensure all possible causes of faults have been eliminated/rectified.

THERMAL FUSES

Many small appliances now have this type of overheat protection device. It can also be found in some makes of washerdrier and tumbledrier machines. It is essentially a failsafe device which when actuated by a predetermined temperature goes open circuit. Once open circuit, it cannot selfset or be manually reset, therefore renewal of the thermal fuse is required once the device has gone open circuit. Renew the thermal fuse only when the fault which caused it to operate has been corrected.

It is a solid-state device and as such contains no moving parts or contacts that may in themselves fail. Thermal fuses alleviate the possibility of fault cycling, are cheap and in most instances easy to fit. They are small but easily recognisable and are often housed in protective sheaths or mouldings.

There is a wide variety of temperature ratings available to suit the various applications, so great care must be taken when replacing the device to match the original rating. The rating is usually printed on the outer casing of the device. **Note:** The metal outer is not insulated and will be at mains voltage when in use, therefore ensure that all mounts, fixings and covers and correctly replaced.

Chapter 23

Drying components and faults (washerdriers)

Combined fan motor, housing and heater detached from the large Ariston drying group of components.

As previously stated in the book, combined washerdriers, both condenser and vented versions, are largely based on their wash-only predecessors. The aim of this section of the book is to look at the components that turn the ordinary automatic washing machine into a washerdrier. The additional parts are often referred to as the 'drying group' or 'ventilation group'. Each part will be looked at independently and as a whole. Reference to other sections within the book, e.g. thermostats, heaters, motors, etc., will also be necessary. Although there are numerous variations in design and positioning of the components in the combination washerdriers, they are all based on the two basic types. A. vented types which draw air in from the surrounding atmosphere, heat it, circulate it through the previously spun wash load and vent the resulting moisture laden air from the machine (similar operation to simple dry-only machines). B. condenser types which use a

sealed warm air circulation system combined with a condenser unit to remove the resulting moisture from the airflow.

As the descriptive diagrams show, both systems have many parts in common with one another. Both the diagrams show a common configuration of fan assembly and heater ducting mounted on the upper portion of the outer tub. However, although this configuration is found in a wide variety of makes and models, there are many variations of component positions possible, as can be seen from the accompanying photographs. A breakdown of the various components of both types of system is as follows.

HEATER UNIT

This unit is of metal construction (usually die-cast aluminium). Housed within it are the heating elements (sheathed type) used to heat the air prior to it entering the inner drum. Often the unit forms the inlet

ducting to the drum via the door seal, but variations can be found which have direct access to the drum via the outer tub. Some machines incorporate a flap within the ducting to prevent steam produced during the normal wash cycle condensing within the heater unit. Air flow during the dry cycle pushes the flap valve open. It is possible for the flap to stick in the closed position and cause overheating within the duct. If your machine has such a flap/valve, check that it is free to move.

Insulation materials (aluminium foil and fibre glass) are often found covering the unit. Ensure that if fitted, it is in good condition and if it has to be disturbed avoid skin contact or inhalation of the insulation material. **Note:** Make sure that the aluminium foil and the metal tape which is used to secure it are clear of all components and electrical connections.

Should element failure occur within the unit, some manufacturers will supply individual spares, whereas

WATER AND CONDENSATE

MOISTURE LADEN AIR

HOT AIR

A. Cold water inlet supply.
B. Triple cold valve with one outlet for reduced condenser supply.
C. Fan motor and housing unit.
D. Heater duct containing heater element(s).
E. External condenser unit with drain hose to fan housing (in case of condensate build-up).
F. Normal outlet pump.
G. Normal outlet hose.
H. Self-cleaning filter in sump hose ducting (if fitted).

This illustration shows one of a number of variations of condenser systems that are to be found. This system utilises the existing sump hose in place of an extra tub access point. Also included is a self-cleaning filter – see text for detail.

others will only supply a heater unit complete with elements. There are normally two elements which allow for delicate or high heat during the drying cycle. Overheat thermostats, T.O.C.s or thermistors are also mounted upon or within the unit. The removal of fixing screws or bolts will allow most heater units to split into two parts. If the unit is to be dismantled for any reason (element renewal or blockage, etc.), inspect the joint closely as many are sealed with heat and steam resistant sealant which once disturbed, must be renewed. With the condenser machines (sealed systems), it is possible under some circumstances for fluff to build up within the unit at various points. As with the dry-only machines, it is advisable to check for such build-ups regularly in order to avoid problems developing.

FAN, MOTOR AND HOUSING UNIT

The fan, motor and housing may be either an integral part of the heater unit casing or condenser unit, or a separate motor and fan housing fixed to the heater unit. In the case of condenser machines, the unit may form the link between the condenser unit and the heater unit. The fan housing may be made of cast aluminium or injection moulded plastic depending on the make and model of machine. Fan chambers on condenser machines often have mounting positions for thermostats or thermistors to monitor the temperature of the air being circulated within the sealed system. Like the heater unit on condenser machines, it is possible for fluff and lint to accumulate within the fan housing or at the inlet and exit points. With care most units can

be dismantled for cleaning, inspection or repair. However, as with the heater unit, heat and steam resistant sealant may have been used during the assembly of the unit. It is essential that any such sealant is renewed with a suitably resistant replacement once it has been disturbed. The lower portion of the fan housing usually has a small drain hole to allow any condensation entering the chamber to drain away. Ensure that this is clear of any blockage.

Within the fan chamber, fixed directly to the fan drive motor shaft will be a centrifugal (barrel style) fan. Various types of fan to shaft fixings are used, threaded shaft and nut, slide fit and grub screw, and taper and collet. The blades of the fan should be kept clean and if it is removed for any reason, (e.g. removing fluff build up from rear), make sure it is correctly re-positioned on the shaft to avoid jamming or chafing when the fan assembly is rebuilt.

Motors used to rotate the fan can be one of three types, shaded pole induction, asynchronous induction motor (capacitor start) and series wound brush motor. Some of the more common problems that may occur with all of these motors are as follows:

Shaded pole induction. Failure of one or both motor bearing(s) allows the rotor to foul the stator. Fluff, or the fan out of position causes the motor to stall and overheat or burn out if not fitted with a T.O.C. The main benefit of this type of motor is that it is quiet when running and is relatively cheap to buy.

Asynchronous induction. This has a low starting torque. Failure of the capacitor results in overheating of the motor windings, otherwise it is reliable and quiet.

Brush motor. These are prone to brush wear or sticking brushes. It is noisy in operation.

CONDENSER UNIT

The removal of moisture from the air flow within the condenser machines is by the creation of a cold area within the sealed system upon which the moisture held in the warm air flow can condense. The area used for this purpose can either be A. internal, i.e. within the gap between the outer tub and drum or B. external, i.e. being an independent unit, usually of semi-transparent plastic material, fixed to the outer of the tub unit or inner of the shell of the machine, but being so connected as to form part of the sealed air flow system. The latter is the more common version of the two. For condensing purposes both systems are kept cold by the introduction of a controlled flow of cold water. To be effective in removing the large amount of moisture from the air flow, the water introduced to the system must cool a large area. Therefore, the water entering the system may pass through either a trickle bar, or the entry point may be so designed as to create a capillary action or spray. Each system creates a broad but thin film of cold water within the condenser unit or tub of the machine. The design and construction of each system allows both the cold water supplied to the unit and the condensate (steam now condensed into liquid) to collect in either the sump of the outer tub or separate sump of the condenser unit. Periodical operation of the normal outlet pump is then all that is required to discharge the water via the normal outlet hose. The now much cooler air, having had the moisture removed from it, is once again recirculated via the fan over the heaters. The time taken to dry the recommended load sizes depends on the efficiency of this sealed system, correct loading and setting of the drying time.

Shown is the large condenser drier unit from an Ariston combined machine. The whole unit fits into the space around the outer tub unit A double door seal is used in this instance with the large circular metal inlet duct (C) sandwiched between.

A. Restricted cold supply to condenser unit.
B. Large condenser moulding.
C. Inlet duct.
D. Heater duct.
E. Fan housing and motor.
F. Air return duct from condenser unit to fan.
G. Condenser inlet from outer tub. (Warm moist air)
H. Water/condensate outlet to sump hose/pump.

This vented combined washerdrier has an unusual but functional drying arrangement. The heating elements are housed within the all metal door. The fan and motor are located on the front underside of the machine (see air intake vents at front left-hand side). Air is drawn in via the front vents by the fan unit and ducted into the door cavity at an entry point below the door seal. The heated air then enters the drum from the centre of the door protrusion, passes through the wash load and exits via two rear vent hoses. The two rear vent hoses are connected to the outer tub unit and outer shell of the machine where two large filters are located. Inlet filters are also included to eliminate particles entering the heater duct and a flap valve is located on the exit of the heater ducting to eliminate water/steam ingression during normal wash and spin actions of the machine.

pumps to discharge any fluff produced during drying down the normal drain/outlet. Some machines have a means of flushing the condenser unit during the water intake of the normal wash cycles. This is normally done by diverting the cold inlet so that both soap dispenser and condenser unit receive unrestricted water supply from the cold inlet valve during filling for wash and rinse cycles. The aim is to flush any fluff/lint that has built up within the unit down into the filter or sump ready to be removed or discharged during normal operation of the machine. In reality, only a portion of the condenser unit is capable of being flushed in this way, so build-ups and blockages can still occur. Some machines (mainly in the Servis/Hitachi range) have a filter housed within the sump hose ducting which are designed to be self-cleaning by the water passing back and forth within the hose during the

Unlike the vented machines, sealed condenser systems do not have user accessible fluff/lint filters within the air flow. Some rely on the normal sump/filter to do the job, whereas other machines have efficient outlet

Most heater ducts are insulated and foil covered. Ensure that it is in good condition and sealed correctly.

With fixings and insulation removed, the casing could then be split into its two halves. This revealed that the lower element had failed and that damage had occurred to the aluminium ducting. A complete unit was therefore required along with thorough inspection of all other components.

With the fan unit removed from the machine, positioning marks were made prior to stripdown (to ensure correct assembly).

The unit was easily stripped down for cleaning/inspection. The fan in this instance was secured to the motor shaft by a brass collet. Once the nut had been slackened a sharp tap freed it from the shaft.

The motor bearings were thoroughly checked for wear or excessive play and for free rotation. The whole unit was cleaned and correctly sealed prior to refitting to the machine.

wash action rotations. However, blockages can occur if used to dry several loads without wash cycles in between. If these machines are to be used for continuous dry-only cycles, it would perhaps be wise to intersperse the dry cycles with a short wash cycle (with or without load) in order to keep the fixed filter clear. See your instruction booklet for details.

As with all components forming the condenser system, sealant may have been used at certain points to prevent leaks (both water and air). It is essential that any such sealant is renewed during assembly with a sealant identical to the original.

This Zanussi combined condenser washerdrier does not have any external drying components other than a timer. There is no fan, fan housing or fan motor. Heating for the dry cycle is by the three sheathed heaters mounted in the top left quarter of the tub (above the normal water level) The hose on the right of the outer tub supplies water to a trickle bar mounted within the outer tub. The load is rotated near the heat source, i.e. the three heaters, whilst the opposite side of the tub is kept cool by the cold water trickle. The process does work but drying times can be very lengthy.

This is a close up of a rear mounted condenser unit. The ribbed hose on the right is the restricted cold supply and the hose to the centre is used to flush the condenser unit during normal fill sequences of wash and rinse.

The Hotpoint condenser washerdrier uses a universal brush motor to drive the air circulation fan. Brush wear and sticking is not uncommon. Brushes are available as spares but other faults require a complete motor unit as shown.

POOR DRYING PERFORMANCE SEQUENCE (CONDENSER MACHINES)

1. Check that the machine is not overloaded, most can only dry half of what they wash. Read the handbook.
2. Ensure the cold water supply is turned on. Condenser machines require a cold water supply during the dry cycle.
3. Check that the fan and heaters are OK. Functional testing should prove this. If in doubt, check the continuity of heater and free movement of the circulation fan.
4. Check that a trickle of water is passing through the condenser unit, NOT DRIPS!
Note: A water flow of less than .35 litres per minute (1 pint in 100 seconds) will cause ineffective drying in most machines. This will usually occur only with tank-fed cold supplies. Remember the installation requirements of minimum head of water. Also blockages or restrictions to the valve filter, reducer or spray/trickle bar may cause the flow to be too slow.

If the first four checks prove to be OK, then follow the next steps in the order in which they are set out.

1. Check removable pump filter (if fitted) or sump hose catch pot or self-cleaning filter for restrictions. Clean as necessary.
2. Check that the pump operates correctly and discharges a full load of water well within the allotted time, i.e. 1 minute – if in doubt check pump and hoses for blockages. Remember, pumps with T.O.C.s may trip part way through the dry cycle owing to overheating on the long combined cycle. See Pumps chapter.
3. Check that the flow rate through the condenser is not too fast. If too much water is entering the chamber it may be picked up by the air flow and deposited on the wash load.
4. Check the water flow through the condenser unit is evenly spread (by capillary action) giving as large a cool surface area as possible. **Note:** Such observations are not possible on all machines, only those with transparent condenser units. If observation is required it must be done at a safe distance via an RCD protected supply, and with only the minimum of panels removed. Isolate for all other checks, before refitting panels or continuing with further testing. Please note, this is the only test throughout the book that may require observation whilst the machine is in operation.
5. If possible try to observe if water droplets are being blown through the inlet duct, e.g. spots on glass or entry point.
6. If droplets are seen to be deposited and the water flow appears correct through the condenser unit, a fluff blockage maybe the cause. Strip down the unit and clean it thoroughly. Some machines have an extra hose to the unit to flush any fluff away. Problems can also arise from long hair, animal hair and wool. Check all connections and hoses, etc. Ensure that parts fitted originally with sealant are resealed with the correct sealant. If this is not done, a vapour leak could occur and result in failure of other items or low insulation.
7. If all the above tests prove to be correct, the fault may lie in a small weep from one of the inlet valves, i.e. failing to close correctly. This may wet the wash load via the dispenser as the drying cycle works normally. Check for weeping valves by process of elimination. With the machine electrically isolated, remove each hose in turn from its corresponding valve and observe the valve outlet. A little water will be spilt during the removal of the hose and care must be taken to mop it up immediately. Observe the outlet closely (perhaps for some minutes). After the initial spillage, there should be no more water. When a constant drip is observed you have found the offending valve. Although the machine is electrically isolated, the water supply to the valves will need to be on for this type of test.

If condensation is found at any time under the top cover of the machine (which may be accompanied by white scale deposits in hard water areas), the cause could be a warm air leak (vapour leak) from the fan housing, heater ducting, inlet point at the door seal or thermostats. Ensure all are correctly positioned and sealed. **Note:** Leaks on seals or gaskets may be due to imperfections in mouldings or wraggs left during manufacture. Carefully remove and smooth any such defects and ensure a good seal is obtained. Some manufacturers use a sealant compound at these points; ensure that only the correct heat resistant sealant is used and do not refit seals without compound if it had been used on the original seal.

SAFETY POINTS

1. Always ensure the mains electrical supply is isolated – switched off and plug out – when checking. If observing a water flow test, do so with the use of an RCD protected circuit and test its operation before use.
2. Fully isolate the machine before commencing further investigations, stripdown or repair.
3. Ensure moving parts like the blower motor and fan have stopped before continuing with fault finding.
4. Ensure the drier heating elements have cooled prior to checking or stripdown. Also check that the door glass and ducting have cooled sufficiently before you touch them.

Chapter 24

Timers (programmers)

E.T.N. style timer with two internally mounted motors, one on each side.

Fig 1 Thermostop coil in de-energised mode preventing timer cam advancing until temperature required closes thermostat and supplies the coil with power.

Two timers are normally used on combined washerdrier machines — one for programme selection (knob on the right) and one for selecting the length of the drying cycle (knob on the left).

The programmer or timer, as it is more commonly known, is the unit located at the top of the machine, directly behind the selector knob on mechanically controlled machines, whereas machines that are controlled electronically may have the programmers split into two or more circuit boards, modules as they are usually known.

Note: The diagrams depict a thermostop system operating with normally open stats (N.O.). Versions with normally closed stats (N.C.) will work in a reverse manner to that shown, i.e. when energised main cam advance prevented and when de-energised, main cam advance allowed. Both variations can be found — be aware of the way your particular system functions.

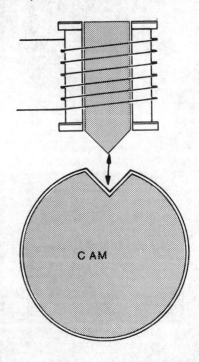

Fig 2 Thermostop coil in energised mode allowing the advancement of main cam barrel i.e. thermostat closed and supplying power to coil.

Internal view of thermostop type timer. Main cam barrel right, narrower timing and motor reversal cam centre and thermostop coil and mechanism on the left.

Early and late Crouzet type timers. The timer on the left has individual push on connectors whereas the timer on the right has round pin block connectors to one side only and is therefore much easier to fit.

Block connectors like the one shown are becoming more popular. Five individual connectors are used on this timer and must be fitted correctly. Ensure that connections within the block do not push out when fitted.

This timer from a Hotpoint machine has both edge connectors and individual amp tag connections to the front switches.

When a programme is selected, the timer (mechanical or electronic) follows a pre-determined sequence switching components in and out (i.e. heater, pump, valves), for various lengths of time. Owing to the apparent complexity of this component, it wrongly tends to be regarded as a "NO GO" area.

The intention of this manual has been to show that the automatic washing machine is not so mysterious, and when broken down into its constituent parts, its simplicity of operation is revealed. To describe the working of the timer in your particular machine would require the make, model number, date of manufacture and the timer number itself. These are needed to ascertain which variation of timer and associated variation of programmes that your particular machine has. In their most infinite wisdom, the manufacturers have seen fit to change their timers, numbers and wiring colours, etc, with regularity.

Timers cannot be repaired. Complete unit changes are needed for internal timer faults. However, on some timers, drive motor coils can be renewed if a simple open circuit has occurred, see: Using a meter chapter.

Without detailed information of the switching sequences of the faulty timer, internal faults are difficult to trace.

Units can often be difficult to fit, unless a logical approach is used!

The main benefits of timers

(a) Modern timers are very reliable

(b) New units can be relatively low in cost, although this differs from make to make of appliance. Having said that, the price variations for similar parts (e.g. only the cam barrel on some makes is different) between some brands can be extremely wide.

It must be remembered that when a fault is suspected, it is not always the most complicated component that can cause the most trouble. If a process of elimination is used and all other parts of the machine are found to be working correctly, it is only then that the timer should be suspected. (Unless of course in the case of obvious failure, such as a burn out or damage to the timer.) **Note:** Ensure that the power is turned off and that the plug is removed from its socket at all times. Do not remove the timer from the machine at this point.

The removal and subsequent exchange of the timer can be a long and tedious task on some machines, and should not be undertaken lightly. However, several of the more modern machines have improved the way in which the wiring harness is fitted to the timer. Multi-block connectors are now used on many machines making timer renewal much easier. Do not fall into the trap of replacing the timer because of the ease of the job. Correct diagnosis of the fault and a methodical approach to both fault finding and perhaps subsequent replacement of the timer is essential.

Do not remove any wiring as yet, but thoroughly check for any overheating of the connections to and from the timer spades (connections), i.e. if a fault is suspected in the heater switch, trace the wire from the heater to the timer. This gives the location of the heater switch and should be examined for any signs of burning or being loose. This would at least confirm your suspicions.

Having decided that the timer is at fault, a note should be taken of all of the numbers that are on the timer, together with the make, model, serial number and age of your machine.

Armed with this information, you can obtain an EXACT replacement. When the replacement has been obtained, visually check that they are identical, as timers will not be exchanged by any known company, once they have been fitted. You have been warned! Having confirmed that it is the correct replacement, and any

In some instances it is possible to renew the timer motor coil if it is found to be open circuit. Do not mix the motors as they normally rotate in different directions. Insert a small flat-bladed screwdriver under the retaining spring clip and lift it slightly.

Mark the correct motor position and lift the motor free.

With the clip eased, slide it sideways to free it from its position.

accompanying documents have been read thoroughly, you can proceed to swap the wiring. The only way that this can be done is by placing the new timer in the same plane as the original, swapping the wires or block connectors on a one-to-one basis. (Although very time consuming, this is by far the safest method). Alternatively tag each wire with its corresponding timer connection number, i.e. 2H, 3B etc., prior to removal. A mistake at this point would be almost impossible to rectify

without a wiring and timer diagram, therefore it is advisable to ask a colleague to supervise operations. When all connections have been successfully exchanged, the timer can be fitted into position, ensuring that any parts that are connected to door interlocks, etc., are positioned correctly, then double check the work carried out and earth continuity. Once fitted into position, and the covers have been refitted, the power can be turned on, and a functional test programme can be implemented.

Note: Some timers have small metal clips that join/link terminals together. These generally do not come with the new timer. Ensure they are swapped from the original.

Insert the small flat-bladed screwdriver between the two halves of the motor casing and ease them apart.

The two halves of the casing will part to expose the coil and permanent magnet rotor.

The coil can now be removed from its position. Ensure that the small plastic anti-reverse mechanism is in its correct position in the base of the casing.

Fit the new coil making sure that it is the right way around.

Re-assemble both halves and press firmly together to ensure that they locate correctly. Check that the motor rotates correctly (in only one direction) as original. The motor can now be refitted to the timer — a reversal of the removal procedure. Note: This sequence can be carried out with the timer in situ, it was removed in this instance for photographic purposes only.

Typical timer with thermostop coil and plate to lower right-hand side. The single timer motor and thermostop mechanism is clearly visible with the rear cover removed. Timer coil renewal is also possible on this type of timer.

Timers (programmers)

This AKO timer has an exposed thermostop coil and slide operating a plastic arm.

Temperature plus time programmer in situ in this condenser washerdrier machine.

Cam Follower Down = A-C
Connections Made

Edge Cam Switch

Cam Follower Up = A-B
Connections Made

Cam Follower

Switch as A-B
As A-C

Etched Disc

Face cam timer.

Types of timer internal switches.

COMPUTER CONTROLLED MACHINES (ELECTRONIC TIMERS)

The functional parts of these machines, i.e. motor, drum, pump, etc., differ little from machines with conventional selector knobs and mechanical timers. Micro-processor controlled machines are easily recognisable by their digital displays used to indicate the programme selection. Most have the ability to display an error code when faults occur which relate to a table in the hand book. Faults within micro-processor timer circuitry can be difficult to locate as the complex circuit board components cannot be easily checked. It is best to eliminate all other possible causes of faults before suspecting either the power module or programme unit. If all the other checks prove satisfactory, then check all connections to and from the control boards, (micro-processor machines generally have two* – one low voltage board for the micro-processor, selector panel and display, and one power board with transformer, relays and thyristors to operate the mains voltage switching which the processor

A.

B.

C.

The two photographs above depict a typical computer controlled machine facia with selector buttons and L.E.D. display (A). Photograph (B) is the same facia panel removed to expose the main programme circuit board housed behind it. Photograph (C) shows both programme board and matching power module from the same machine.

cannot do directly. ***Note**: Washerdrier computer controlled machines may have three boards. The third board being used for auto sensing of the dry cycle. The connections to printed circuit boards are prone to oxidization giving poor electrical contact especially on the low voltages used by the programme boards. Check closely for poor connections. If the fault remains after all other components have been checked and found to be OK, the only option left is to change one or other (or in some instances, both) of the circuit boards. Owing to the way in which the power board functions, (see following paragraph), it is most likely to be a failure in this circuitry or its components at fault.

The power board is generally much bulkier than the programme board and houses a large transformer to drop the voltage to the processor. Electronic circuit faults occur more often with power boards as the mains switching operating the pump, heater, etc., is switched mechanically by relays or electronically by thyristors operated by the lower voltage supplied from the programme board, i.e. processors themselves cannot directly switch mains power and use mechanical relays or thyristors. Try to isolate if a mechanical fault is suspected, (e.g. heater not receiving power, maybe a sticking/faulty relay, etc.) Items that short circuit and blow fuses may also damage

This internal view of a computer-controlled machine (wash only model) shows the programme module in place behind the front facia of the machine. The printed circuit board is clearly seen as is the P.C.B. edge connectors. Note in this machine the wiring leading to the power module is ordinary cable not ribbon cable.

The power module in this instance is located in the bottom right-hand side of the machine. Wiring to and from the unit is clearly visible.

Power module removed from machine showing complex circuitry of this unit. This particular unit was severely damaged by a simple short circuit of the pump wiring. The fault damaged several circuit board components and the circuitry of the board itself. The simple fault resulted in a complete new unit being required.

their control relay or thyristor. For instance, a simple fault such as the live supply to the outlet pump breaking loose during a spin cycle and touching the earthed metal shell of the machine would result in a direct short circuit. Such a fault on a machine with a mechanical timer would blow the appliance fuse in the socket and rectification would be straight forward. However, the same fault on a micro-processor controlled machine is likely to damage the components of the circuit board used to switch the pump supply, resulting in a much more expensive repair.

The programme board may also be referred to as the display board or module. It differs from the power module in that it is much slimmer (but often much wider) than the power board and lacks the larger components such as relays, transformers, heat sinks, etc.

It is usually mounted behind the front facia of the machine although variation in positioning will be found between manufacturers and models within each range.

Obtaining individual components from the machine manufacturers is not possible as only complete boards/modules

Ribbon cable like that shown is often used to connect programme board with the power board.

are supplied as spares.

Faults within the components or circuitry of the board are extremely difficult to trace and as with the power board, only complete units are supplied by the manufacturer. Before contemplating a board fault, ensure all other components within the machine are OK and that all connections to and from the printed circuit boards are in good condition and are firmly pushed into place. Check thoroughly all connections, wiring and all protective covers. With the machine isolated, look closely at all connections that carry mains voltage when in use, as loose connections can cause overheating and interference which can affect the processor chips. Include all earth path connections in the wiring checks and renew any that are loose, have cracked covers or show signs of damage (e.g. overheated, etc.). Do not forget to include the plug connections.

With persistent or unusual

faults, i.e. intermittent operation, random displays, works for short periods and then blanks memory, etc., check the condition of the supply socket. If a poor connection exists between any pin of the plug and its supply connection, again interference will be present which may corrupt the processor, see Basics – electrical. Renew if suspect.

A faulty suppression unit may also be the cause of such random and difficult to trace faults. Ensure the unit is securely earthed, see Suppressors chapter.

With the need to prevent interference from particular components within the machine items, such as the main wash motor, may have small suppression units called chokes, see Suppressors chapter, which prevent any interference being transmitted along the wiring of the machine. Ensure that any chokes fitted within the machine are secure and in good condition (e.g. check continuity). If all the aforementioned checks prove satisfactory, then it is most likely that the processor chip is corrupted or the board has a fault within its circuitry. Such faults will require a replacement unit. Carefully note

all connections to and from the unit and keeping in mind the paragraph regarding handling of the unit, remove it from the machine. Inspect it closely for dirt or debris which may be affecting the circuit or its components. If any dirt is present, it should be blown free (do not use metal items such as screwdrivers). Check the board for cracks or possible moisture damage due to faulty covers etc. Before finally accepting that a new unit is needed, it would be wise to inspect the printed circuit board's soldered connections to verify that they are sound, i.e. loose or poor connections, called dry joints, can often be easily rectified. If all these checks prove negative, a new unit will be necessary. Take care to fit the unit correctly on all its mounts and ensure all covers and connections are sound. Take particular care to avoid direct contact with the components of the unit.

Do not touch the processor board's components at all as they are sensitive to static electricity and are easily damaged by careless handling. The power boards are more robust but care must still be exercised when handling them.

Test ribbon cable continuity by inserting a metal plate in one connection and testing individual wire at the other. A low voltage test meter is essential for this type of test. Move the whole length of the cable on each test to check for intermittent open circuit.

Note: All checks must be carried out with the machine isolated in the usual manner with the taps off and the plug out! Under no circumstances should you try to test the processor board even with a low 9 volt or similar tester because the micro-processor chip can easily be damaged. Use of the 1.5 volt tester is recommended for continuity testing of the wiring between the module units. Try to leave the block connectors in place and using the probes of the tester, check for continuity between exposed printed circuit points close to the connector blocks. This will test both the wiring between the modules (usually ribbon cable) and the connection to the printed circuit board.

Schematic wiring diagram of a simple tumble dry only machine.

TUMBLE DRY ONLY MACHINES

Both mechanical and electronic (micro-processor) controls are now used for controlling drying programmes and their operation is similar to that mentioned in previous sections. The mechanical timers are much simpler as fewer combinations of switches are required. Computer controlled machines, although very similar in basic construction, usually contain some means of sensing the dryness of the load and match this to a preselected setting by the user, e.g. iron dry, fully dry etc. Termination of the

programme occurs when the selected setting is attained thus preventing over drying by warming the load unnecessarily.

MECHANICAL TIMERS

Mechanical timers are by far the most popular type of timer used in the lower and mid price range of tumble dry only machines. They are smaller than the similar timers used in

washing machines, but the cam action of switching is almost the same.

Failure of both the clockwork drive and pitting of switches are the most common faults but there are no individual spare parts available. Repair consists of obtaining a replacement unit. As there are several shaft sizes, hole fixings and timers available make sure that the correct replacement is obtained and

Shown are three versions of mechanical timers. The top timer is clockwork driven and is restricted to tumble dry only machines. The lower two are electrically driven and can be found in both combined machines (vented and condenser types), and tumble dry only machines. Many variations exist but basic function remains the same.

fitted on a one for one basis.

On more recent machines, the clockwork-driven timer has been replaced by an electrically-powered motor to drive the timer. As with the previous type no individual parts are available for these timers, therefore with any fault they must be replaced with a complete new unit. In common with all timers, although they all may look the same externally, there are many different combinations possible; fixing points, terminal positions, shaft sizes and length of selectable time, all of which differ with each make and model of machine. It is therefore essential that an exact replacement is obtained.

The clockwork version of timer is restricted to tumble dry only machines whereas the motor driven timer can be used for controlling drying times in tumble dry only machines, washerdrier (vented type) and condenser washerdriers. In both types of washerdriers, motor reversal for the main wash motor will be controlled by the main wash timer.

AUTO SENSING DRYING SYSTEMS (COMBINED MACHINES AND DRY ONLY)

Many modern machines, both dry-only and combined types, have the option of drying on either a timed basis or by auto sensing, i.e. to end the dry cycle when the clothes are dry or when they have reached a preselected level of dryness. Auto sensing is a most useful option which leads to more economical use. Several different systems are used in auto sensing machines and what follows is a general description of three of the more common ones in use today. The first can be found in both combined vented machines and some dry-only machines, whereas the second and third versions are at present confined to the more expensive computer controlled models.

1. This simple system monitors the temperature of the air within the outlet duct by means of a bi-metal thermostat. A double thermostat is often used to allow for two levels of dryness to be achieved, i.e. total dry or iron dry (slightly damp to aid ironing). There are also the normal thermostats on the inlet ducting which control the temperature of the air used to dry the clothes and to prevent overheating. A theoretical operation of a combined vented washerdrier would be as follows. The machine, having been set for a dry cycle, starts to blow the heated air through the wash load whilst rotating the drum. The length of the dry cycle, main drum motor control and supply to the drying group are all controlled by the one main timer unit. The main timer is of the thermostop variety (see previous section), and is prevented from advancing the main cam barrel by the intermittent action of the thermostop facility. Supply for the thermostop coil is via either of the exhaust thermostats which are normally closed. Which stat is in circuit depends on the level of dryness required and is set by user switch selection, i.e. total dry or iron dry button.

Air passing into the drum from the heater unit is controlled, in this instance by a 100 degree thermostat, and as it passes through the wet clothing creating the drying effect, its temperature drops. The temperature of the air leaving the drum via the exhaust duct will be appreciably lower but will increase as the clothing dries. The exhaust thermostats monitoring the temperature will have lower settings then the inlet thermostat, in this instance 50 degrees for iron dry and

55 degrees for totally dry. Assuming the iron dry thermostat has been selected to control the thermostop supply, once 50 degrees has been detected in the exhaust duct the thermostat would go open circuit and sever the thermostop supply. With the thermostop now disengaged, the timer is free to move on to the next cam position which would remove power to the drier heaters. A cool tumble would then take place for a predetermined time prior to the machine automatically switching off. This system is simple yet effective and does not require a separate drying time to be set by the user, only the level of dryness required needs to be selected. For this system to work on machines without a thermostop facility, i.e. timers with two motors, one for timing/motor rotation and the other for cam advance. Normally open thermostats would be used at the exhaust duct. These thermostats would close at the preselected temperature and supply power to the cam advance motor to move the main cam barrel on to the next position where the end sequence would then be similar to that described.

2. With this system a microprocessor is used to monitor both inlet and exhaust temperature. Measurement is by means of thermistors mounted at both inlet and outlet points. The resistances of both thermistors are monitored by the processor which calculates the temperature differential between them. When the drying cycle commences, both thermistors have relatively the same resistance. However, the inlet temperature will quickly rise to its constant working temperature/resistance, whereas the exhaust temperature/resistance will rise slowly in proportion to the dryness of the load until a preselected

temperature/resistance differential value is attained.

The programme of the processor has resistance variations built into it corresponding to the required levels of dryness of the load depending on which level has been selected by the user. When the corresponding resistance is achieved, the processor will proceed to complete the next step in sequence, i.e. heater off, cool tumble for set time. Both this system and the following one can have a greater range of dryness settings available which are either user selectable or in the case of combined machines, matched to the wash selected, e.g. delicate, cottons, etc.

3. The third system is again part of a micro-processor or module controlled circuit similar to No.2. Sensing however is somewhat different in that the detection of the required level of dryness is not governed by temperature. This system monitors the moisture content of the load as it rotates in the warm air flow. The electrical resistance of the load is proportional to how wet/damp it is, i.e. when wet, low resistance as water is a good conductor of electricity, and when dry, high resistance (little water to allow electrical flow). The sensing system may sound complex but in fact is quite simple. A metal probe, usually a simple domed bolt, is mounted on the drum surface at a point where it will make contact with the load as the drum rotates. The probe (bolt) is insulated from the metal drum by plastic washers and is electrically connected to the module or micro-processor timer. Owing to the need for the drum to rotate, a moving contact system is employed at some point in the circuit which usually consists of a bus bar and phosphor bronze bush. Within the circuit is a bleed resistor, the function of which is to dissipate any static build up in order to prevent it from being transmitted to the electronic control circuitry where it could cause damage.

The monitoring probe is part of the electronic circuitry and as such, only operates at 5 volts. The resulting variations in resistance are used in a similar way as that previously described in 2.

Note: When testing systems that contain micro- processor controls, ensure that all continuity testing is carried out with a low voltage tester. Do not exceed 9 volts when continuity testing

Before suspecting a fault in the control module, read through the previous section on computer controlled machines, and the Timers chapter. Then check the following:
1. The filter is clean and free from lint/fluff.
2. The vent/hose is not blocked or obstructed.
3. Inlet is not blocked/obstructed.
4. T.O.C.s and fixed thermostats, connections and wiring.
5. Continuity of elements.
6. Firm contact on movable connection on probe circuit.
7. That insulation on probe head is intact, i.e. no cracks etc.
8. All control board edge connectors.
9. If pressure system (see dry-only machines section), ensure all seals and panels are fitted correctly to prevent air leaks.
10. Ensure that the circulation fan is not jammed. The fan on some machines may be driven by a belt. Make sure that it is intact and not slack (some belts are elasticated and tend to stretch). Renew if suspect. Some machines may have the circulation fan fitted to the motor shaft. Ensure that it has not worked loose from the shaft.

On computer-controlled machines, many of the faults shown may be indicated by a code which is displayed on the front of the machine. Codes differ from machine to machine so refer to your handbook to ascertain the meaning of each code.

Chapter 25

Suspension

During the normal washing and spin drying operations of front loading machines of all types, a great deal of vibration is produced. The level of vibration increases during the spin sequences, especially if the wash load is out of balance or severely under loaded. If the outer tub unit was fixed rigidly to the shell/outer casing of the machine, damage would be caused to both internal components and to the immediate location of the machine through excessive movement of the free-standing machine.

To avoid the transference of vibration produced during wash and spin cycles, the inner tub unit of front-loading washing machines and washerdriers is supported within the shell/outer casing of the machine by vibration absorbing supports, i.e. suspension. Due to the confines of the shell/outer casing of the modern machine, a limited amount of movement is allowed, but any excessive vibration and movement of the tub unit is removed (damped) by the action of the suspension system supporting the unit.
Note: To prevent damage to components within the machine during transportation/delivery, some means of packing will be fixed to the machine to stop any movement of the tub unit, i.e. rocking suspension. It is essential that any such packing

or transit fixings, as they are commonly known, are removed. There are as many different types of transit packing as there are machines so read your instruction booklet for a description of how to remove the packing from your new machine. It is advisable to retain these instructions and packing should it become necessary to

transport your washing machine again, e.g. moving house. If you do need to refit the transit packing, a good idea is to put a sticker on the door reminding you that the machine must not be used until the packaging has been removed.

Remember, the suspension is the system that controls all of the movement of the tub unit when it is in use. Without the suspension or when it is damaged, the whole tub unit will move violently when in use. See also: Out of balance detection later in this chapter.

WHAT DIFFERENT TYPES OF SUSPENSION ARE THERE?

The spring type suspension, which is simply large strong support springs used only on early slow spin machines.

Large concrete or metal counter-weights are used to improve balance during spin. The position of such weights vary greatly between makes. Ensure they are securely anchored and cannot work loose. Loose weights give rise to noises similar to bearing failure. If left unattended, serious outer tub damage will result. Pictured is a Candy outer tub unit which has both top and lower front weights.

1. View of spring and slide suspension. This is prone to softening of the rubber mount at the top of the suspension leg. The result is a common condition known as twisted tub.

2. To renew the top rubber, the whole unit will have to be withdrawn. Grip the shaft through the spring at the top only, using adjustable pliers inserted through spring.

Slide and spring damper suspension supports the tub from beneath with only small springs or straps at the top for holding the tub unit in mid fore and aft position.

3. Whilst gripping the metal shaft tightly, the securing nut can be removed. (Right hand thread). Note the correct assembly of parts and pull spring downwards to remove top bush. Do not be tempted to renew one side only – you must renew both sides!

*SPRING ONLY UNIT
HOOVER TYPE*

SLIDE AND DAMPER TYPES

The main faults to check for are those of guide wear, allowing the shaft to jump out of position, and also the top rubbers to soften or wear. This results in a phenomenon called 'twisted tub'. The reason for this is the suspension on one side of the tub is not correctly positioned, therefore allowing one side of the tub to bang on the side of the shell and cause damage. A noise fault can also become apparent at the top of the suspension due to soapy water seeping into the suspension via the dispenser or dispenser hose. This is best removed by a spray of lubricant/moisture repellant and an application of Molycote to the top bush and slides. The top and the guides of the suspension are the only parts that should be lubricated in this way.

When fitting top rubbers, the machine should be laid on its face, and the suspension should be held tightly with grips at the top end only. The top nut can then be undone. Do not hold the bottom of the shaft as any marks will quickly wear the plastic guides. When refitting, thoroughly clean the metal shaft and apply a smear of Molycote lubricant paste to the shaft and upper shaped washers. The

Friction pads from various machines. Top section is pad and mount for Zanussi, middle section pad for Indesit, and lower is square pad for Candy.

plastic slides should also have the same paste applied prior to refitting.

THE FRICTION DAMPER SYSTEM

The friction damper system is not unlike the disc braking

system on a motor car. Two support rubbers with asbestos (or similar material) pads are mounted in two spring steel arms. These rest either side of the flat plate attached to the outer tub. When the outer tub moves, the action is slowed down (damped) by the friction of the pads against the plate. This is a very cheap and very effective form of suspension.

When this type of damper is worn, the tub will move excessively and possibly emit a squeaking noise. The noise will be caused by the rubber pad mounts coming into contact with the moving plate, due to the friction material being worn. This is easily overcome by the renewal of the pads themselves. After isolating the machine it should be laid on its back or side to enable the steel spring arms to be opened. When opened, the pads can be prized from their ball and socket joint. **Note**: If the pads on this system become glazed and/or shiny on their contact faces, a chattering sound will be noticed. It may be possible to avoid renewal, by slightly roughening the faces with sandpaper to remove the

Friction type damper.

A friction damper system from a Fagor machine. This is viewed in situ, as the complete front panel can be removed. The front panel removal can be achieved easily by removing the lower panel and two securing screws.
Do not lubricate this type of suspension.

glazing and then refit. If unsuccessful, the pads will have to be renewed. Do not under any circumstances put oil or grease on friction damper systems. Do not inhale the dust from the friction pads as this can be harmful to the lungs. Moisten with water during removal and cleaning to avoid airborne dust particles. Do not blow them clean. Dispose of old pads safely and wash hands after contact.

THE DAMPER AND SPRING SYSTEM

The damper type system is similar to the shock absorbers on your car, and they do the same job. If the smaller version of the system is used, the tub will not actually rest on the damper, but will be hung from springs at the top of the tub, using the dampers at the bottom for shock absorption only. In the larger systems however, the tub is held only by much larger dampers at the bottom of the tub, with

LARGE DAMPER & MOUNTS

retaining straps/springs at the top to limit movement fore and aft.

Faults found with this type of solid damper will have the same symptoms as the friction damper system. The only remedy in this case is the complete renewal of the faulty damper. This can be done by laying the machine on to its face, taking the usual care and isolation procedures. Access to the dampers can be gained by removing the back panel, and unbolting the damper from the shell and tub mounts.

THE SPRING ONLY SYSTEM

The spring only system may also be found. The spring or the mounts can be changed separately if required or replaced as a complete unit.
Note: The left and right springs of all systems are usually of different ratings. Be sure to specify the required side when obtaining a replacement. Also, where two small springs are used for fore and aft support during repair, it is possible that they may become dislodged. It is essential that they are refitted correctly. Please examine the correct positions and make

notes of all springs, etc., before you start.

It must be stressed that any combination of these systems maybe found. A damper system may complement a spring system, or a spring system may complement a friction damper system. Please read all sections thoroughly before starting any repair on the suspension system.

The purpose of suspension in the automatic washing machine, whether wash-only or combined washerdrier, is to damp the oscillations of the spring mounted tub and drum unit. Counter-weights of concrete or in some instances iron, are used to help in the overall balance of the unit and to add weight to the appliance to further help in eliminating movement during use (especially spin). The suspension system works the hardest during the distribute (pre-spin) and spin cycles. Under normal load conditions the simple suspension and counter-weight system works well and reduces tub oscillation as long as all components and connections are secure and in good order. However, if a severe out of balance condition occurs because of a mechanical fault, for example worn suspension, under loading, i.e. one bath mat, overloading, i.e. large duvet, or by washing unsuitable items, such as trainer shoes, excessive vibration and damage may result to both the outer cabinet and internal parts due to the suspension being unable to cope with such adverse oscillations of the tub unit within the confines of the shell/cabinet.

All but the earliest of front loading automatic machines have a pre-spin speed or distribute as it is often called, the action of which is to balance out the wash load by rotating it at a pre-set drum speed. The centrifugal force created by the pre-set speed (usually around 83 rpm on the drum) arranges the wash load evenly over the inner surface of the drum prior to acceleration into the spin. However, this process can fail if:

1. A balled load occurs, i.e. the knotting together of items usually as a result of poor loading by bundling all items into the machine together instead of separately. Stopping the machine, removing and replacing the items individually is usually all that is required for this problem. **Note:** It is wise to reset the machine to a rinse position before the spin to allow correct distribution to take place.

2. Underloading occurs when insufficient clothes are in the drum to distribute evenly around the entire surface, i.e. half drum surface covered but other half not, thus giving a flywheel effect when rotated. **Note:** This is a common fault on some machines and aggravated by the user removing items in the hope of improving the matter when in fact extra items are required,

3. Overloading resulting in little or no free movement of the wash load therefore no distribute action is possible. This will also result in a poor wash.

4. An unsuitable wash load of, for instance, trainers, sleeping bags etc., will create severe out of balance situations and subsequently damage to the machine and/or its surroundings. Try to load the machine correctly.

OUT OF BALANCE PROTECTION

The best way to avoid out of balance problems is to load and use the machine correctly, although even having done this, an out of balance situation may still develop. Many modern machines, especially later computer-controlled models now incorporate a means of detecting an out of balance situation and will take steps to rectify it by re-balancing the load by extending the distribute phase or by terminating the acceleration up to full spin speed thus limiting or avoiding further vibration or damage.

HOW DOES OUT OF BALANCE DETECTION WORK?

O.O.B. detection as it is known can be detected two ways:
(a) Electro-mechanically. This method uses light action micro-switches strategically mounted on the edges of the outer tub or on the suspension legs. They may be actuated by a weight on the arm of the micro-switch or by a contact bar, either of which will be adjustable for calibration of O.O.B. movement. The micro-switch is linked into the motor speed module control circuit, See: Motors chapter (speed control). Excessive movement or inertia resulting from an out of balance situation will actuate the micro-switch at a predetermined level. The impulse caused by the micro-switch's operation terminates the build up to the spin speed selected and normally allows only the distribute speed to operate. After a period of time governed by the circuitry of the

module, a spin sequence will be reinstated in the expectation that a second distribute has cleared the O.O.B. problem. If this is not so, the process is repeated. With mechanical programme timers, this process may continue, dependent on the make and model of the machine, until the time allotted for spin has elapsed. Computer-controlled machines are often programmed (See: Timer chapter), to accept only three O.O.B. impulses before terminating the spin or remainder of the programme completely. The setting of the mechanical O.O.B. detection micro-switches differ greatly between the different makes and also between the different models from the same manufacturer, hence no specific adjustment details can be given within this text.
Note: Ensure actuation of micro-switches are free and all connections to and from them are in good order.
(b) Electronic only.
The electronic O.O.B. detection system is at present limited to computer-controlled machines. It is only the detection process which differs from that already described in section a. Detection in this instance is by monitoring the motor speed reference voltage from the tacho coil, See Motors (speed control) chapter. During an out of balance situation the motor speed will vary, i.e. rise and fall on each revolution of the drum proportional to the degree of the imbalance. If this reference exceeds the pre-programmed tolerances for that particular programme setting or spin, a fault sequence similar to that described in section (a) is implemented and distribution occurs. As before, this may be limited to three such cycles before termination of the set programme and in the case of computer-controlled machines, the display of a corresponding fault code.

Chapter 26

Low insulation

WHAT IS LOW INSULATION?

Low insulation is best described as a slight leak to earth of electricity from the wiring of one or more of the components or wiring in an earthed appliance. If very slight, this will not harm the appliance but is an indication of faults to come and should be corrected immediately for safety reasons.

HOW IS IT CAUSED?

This can be caused by normal wear and tear over a long period, resulting in a breakdown of the insulating coating on wiring, motor windings, heater elements, etc. Such a breakdown of insulation may not result in a failure of the part at this point and the appliance may still function as normal. However, this is no excuse to ignore low insulation as failure to trace and rectify low insulation is both foolhardy and in the long run can be costly in both money terms, and above all safety. Faults such as leaking/weeping shaft seals can give rise to water penetrating the motor windings and resulting in low insulation. If not corrected, this could lead to a complete failure of the motor, or worse. A simple renewal of the shaft seal and careful cleaning and drying of the T.O.C. and

windings may be all that is needed to save money and improve safety for all concerned. It is important not to compromise on safety by ignoring such symptoms.

HOW CAN IT BE DETECTED?

When an engineer tests for low insulation, he will use an instrument called a metrohm/low insulation tester. The law requires repair engineers to test for low insulation, and there is a low minimum allowable level. The law requires that the following tests are made by commercial repair engineers.

Between the earth pin and the plug and all earth connection points within the appliance, the maximum resistance should be 1 ohm, i.e. very low resistance, a perfect connection.

With the appliance turned on, but unplugged, test between the live pin on the plug and the earth pin on the plug. The minimum resistance should be 1 megohm, ideally no detectable reading, i.e. very high resistance, no connection at all.

Repeat this test between the neutral and the earth pin of the plug repeating both tests at various programme settings.

Testing of individual components can be carried out easily by removing connections to the suspect item and

connecting one lead to one of the free terminals and one to the earth terminal and testing, minimum resistance should be 1 megohm, then repeat the test using the other connection.

These tests are carried out using a meter designed to test insulation by applying a high voltage (500 v) at a very low amperage for safety to test the insulation quality of the part to which it is connected. It is an unfortunate fact that some engineers do not possess such an instrument, and therefore do not check for low insulation. This does not mean that you should not!

A meter to test for low insulation would cost upwards of one hundred pounds and is therefore out of the reach of most D.I.Y. people. An alternative is to utilise an in line circuit breaker (see Flowchart). The appliance is plugged into the circuit breaker, which is then plugged into the socket, unless an R.C.D. already protects the circuit or socket. As mentioned in Basics – Electrical, the purpose of the device is to detect low insulation or leakage to earth and turn off the power to the appliance. Although this is not the ideal way of testing for low insulation, it will help in locating it and provide safety for the appliance and its user.

It is wise to test R.C.D. systems on a regular basis to ensure they function correctly and are fully operational when needed. Follow the instructions shown on the unit or on the leaflet accompanying the adaptor. If a fault with the unit is suspected it will need to be tested and possibly re-calibrated for maximum performance by a skilled electrician using a special R.C.D. test meter. If a fault is suspected in an R.C.D. unit, have it checked as they are there for your safety.

The use of a R.C.D. in this way is to aid those who do not possess a low insulation test meter. It must be remembered that the units have a wide range of uses and cannot only be used in this manner. R.C.D.s are designed to ensure safety when using appliances or equipment such as lawn mowers (where there is a danger of cutting through the cable), irons, washing machines, etc. (where water and electricity are in close proximity).

If any appliance trips an R.C.D. (or similar) systems, do not use the appliance until the fault has been rectified. If tripping occurs with no appliances or load on the system, then a fault on the house wiring is indicated and the trip switch should not be reset until the fault is found and corrected.

Have your R.C.D. tested regularly by an approved electrician or electricity board to ensure that it functions correctly and safely at the correct speed of no more than 0.4 of a second. Such tests require an R.C.D. test meter that calculates the trip time of the unit. On simple tests the unit may trip but take too long for it to be classified as safe.

A versatile test meter incorporating 500v insulation test facility.

Modern consumer unit with RDC main switch and MCBs on all circuits.

Double socket RCCB for use in home or workshop.

POINTS TO REMEMBER ABOUT LOW INSULATION

Ensure that any disconnection or removal of wires is safe and not earthing via another wire or the metal case of the appliance, etc.

Whilst disconnecting any wires during the testing for low insulation, it should be remembered that the machine must be isolated from the mains at all times and the panels or covers must be replaced before the appliance is re-tested, i.e. **Do not test with exposed wiring**.

Before testing for low insulation using a circuit breaker all earth paths of the appliance should be tested. This is done by connecting a meter between the earth pin of the plug, and all other metal parts of the appliance in turn. Maximum resistance should be 1 ohm. See: Using a meter chapter.

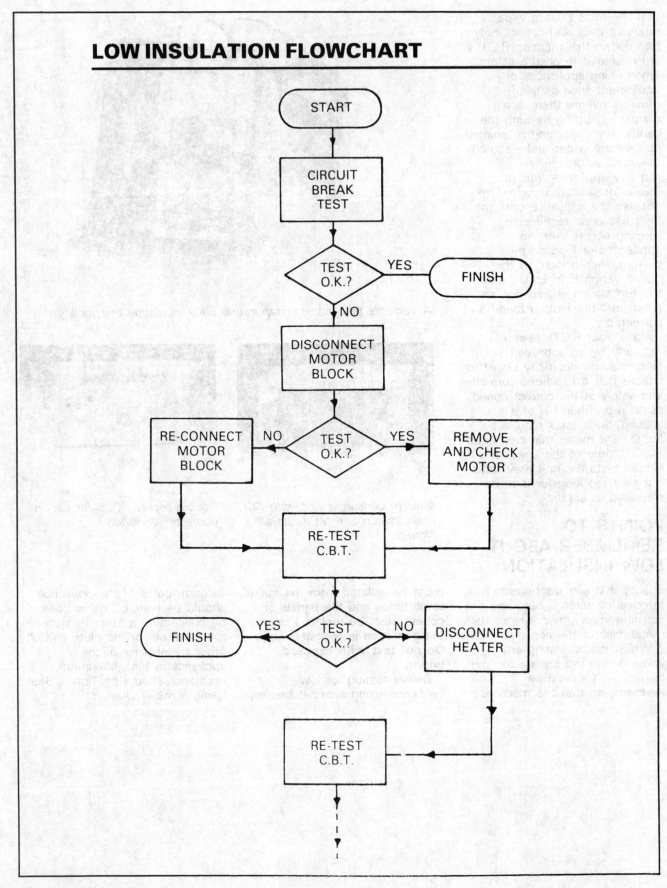

LOW INSULATION FLOWCHART

START

↓

CIRCUIT BREAK TEST

↓

TEST O.K.? — YES → FINISH

↓ NO

DISCONNECT MOTOR BLOCK

↓

RE-CONNECT MOTOR BLOCK ← NO — TEST O.K.? — YES → REMOVE AND CHECK MOTOR

↓ → RE-TEST C.B.T. ←

↓

FINISH ← YES — TEST O.K.? — NO → DISCONNECT HEATER

↓

RE-TEST C.B.T.

↓

Chapter 27

Motors

There are three types of main wash motor used in today's machines; the universal A.C. brush motor, permanent magnet (P.M.) motor and induction motor. **Note:** This chapter covers the range of motors found in combined washerdriers and tumble dry only machines.

WHERE IS THE MAIN MOTOR LOCATED?

On washing machines and combined washerdriers the motor will usually be bolted to the underside of the outer tub. The exception to this is the Hotpoint front loader where the motor can be found bolted to the top left-hand side of the outer tub (viewed from the rear). Tumble dry only machines normally have the main motor mounted on the base of the machine.

WHAT TYPES OF MOTOR ARE THERE?

The following text is a brief introduction into the various types of motors found in use throughout machines in general.

This type of unit normally requires renewal if faulty, although some brushes and patterned armatures are available separately.

BRUSH MOTORS

These normally consist of two sets of electromagnets. An outer fixed set called the field coil, and an inner set free to rotate called the armature. The armature is made up of many separate windings and is configured in such a way that power is only supplied to one set of windings at a time. The corresponding movement induced in the armature, continuously brings a new set of windings into circuit, whilst the previous winding circuit is broken. The windings are continuously out of synchronization, therefore inducing continuous rotation of the armature whenever power is

supplied. Reversal of the motor is normally achieved by reversing the power flow through the armature windings via a set of reversing switches in the timer. This type of motor can be used with alternating current (A.C.) from the mains, or with direct current (D.C.) from a battery, and is often used for the main drive motor in washing machines, especially on machines with spin speed above 1000 rpm.

INDUCTION MOTORS (CAPACITOR/RELAY START)

This type of induction motor has a capacitor/relay to 'kick' the rotor into action by putting a delay into the motor's start windings. The resulting imbalance creates rotation in the direction of the run winding current flow. A reversal of power in the run winding reverses the motor. Speed is governed by the amount of windings supplied with power. Induction motors of this type are found in both washing machines and tumble dry only machines.

Labels: Field Coil, Armature, Commutator, Tacho Coil, Connector Block, Tacho Magnet, Brush Ring, Motor Brush

As all of the work is done by a complicated set of windings in the stator, this motor is generally not repairable and must be changed for a new unit. Capacitor failure often results in the motor failing to run. This can result in burn out as the rest of the motor windings are receiving power but no rotation is possible. Overheat is inevitable, even when T.O.C. (thermal overload cut-out) protected.

Warning: When checking for faults, the machine must always be isolated from the mains. Turn off at the wall socket and remove the plug. The capacitor(s) will still contain a charge although the mains has been isolated. This must be discharged by using an electrically isolated screwdriver. Do this by 'shorting' the terminals of the capacitor with the shaft of the screwdriver ensuring that you are only in contact with the insulated handle. **It is not safe to proceed further until this has been done.**

If the stator windings of an induction motor are faulty, it

Shown is a Fagor motor, typical of the new style induction motors, that are capable of variable speed build up via a module. Note the tacho connector at the rear of the motor.

may continue to run although appearing sluggish and getting extremely hot even when used for a short time. Therefore, if you have been running the machine to determine the fault, proceed with care as the motor will remain hot for some time. If the motor appears to be very hot, the motor winding may be faulty and the unit should be replaced.

THE CAPACITOR – WHAT DOES IT LOOK LIKE?

Capacitors used for motor starting can have either metal or plastic outer casings with an insulated top with two terminals.

The storage capacity of a capacitor is measured in microfarads (μF) and is displayed on the casing of the capacitor.

Typical capacitor for use with induction motors. Do not confuse capacitors with suppression units. They may look similar, but their functions differ.

Any replacement must be of the same µF rating.

If the motor fails to run on wash, but runs on spin and there are two capacitors fitted, it is possible that one of them is faulty. Change the capacitor with the lowest µF rating and re-test. If only one capacitor is fitted then the motor should be checked, see Motors chapter.

If the motor runs on wash but fails on spin and there are two capacitors fitted, there are two possible faults. Change the capacitor with the highest µF rating and re-test, remembering the previous warning about an isolated capacitor retaining an electrical charge. If the door interlock is connected directly to the motor spin circuit, and the door is not closed properly, then the spin will be prevented from operating. A fault within the interlock would also prevent the spin, refer to the Door Switches (interlocks) chapter.

Note: TOC – Thermal Overload Cutout

This means that if the safe working temperature is exceeded, this device will sever the power supply to the motor. Most T.O.C.s are now self re-setting, resulting in constant heating up and cooling down of the motor. If the fault is not spotted quickly, the T.O.C. itself

will fail, resulting in complete motor failure.

THE RELAY – WHAT IS IT?

A relay is an electro-mechanical device used in this particular instance for induction motor starting in place of a capacitor.

WHAT DOES IT LOOK LIKE?

The most common relay consists of a plastic moulding with three terminal tags, two at the top and one at its base. On the centre section is a wire wound coil.

A relay may be placed in circuit to cause the phase displacement necessary to start the induction motor. This is a mechanical delay as described and it is essential that the relay is upright when energized.

HOW DOES IT WORK?

The main aim of the relay in the context of asynchronous induction motors is to cause a delay in the start winding supply, similar to the capacitor. The main difference is that the relay achieves this operation mechanically. The wound coil section is connected in series with the run winding. When power is supplied to the motor, the current to the run winding passes through the coil and on to the motor run winding. This current induces a magnetic force in the coil which in turn attracts the metal core of the relay. The metal core is linked to an internal contact switch and when 'made', allows current to pass to the start winding (see diagram). This operation gives the required delay to induce starting of the induction motor.

When power is switched off, gravity resets the relay core. It is, therefore, essential that the relay is in its correct position and the machine upright for this item to function correctly.

The relay may also be matched to the run winding of the motor, i.e. as initial power draw is high, the magnetic attraction of the relay coil is great enough to attract the core, but when the motor is running, the initial high power draw drops and weakens the magnetic pull of the coil. The core drops and open circuits the start winding allowing the motor to continue running more efficiently. Always make sure

Basic induction motor

that the correct replacement is obtained by quoting model numbers and manufacturer when ordering.

Faults to watch for are, open circuit of the coil, metal core sticking (in either position), and contact points failing. Renew any suspect relay immediately as the failure of this item, like the capacitor, can lead to motor failure.

If you have to renew a damaged stator coil or motor and it is relay started, it is wise

Anticlockwise rotation

Clockwise rotation

Induction motor rotor

to change the relay at the same time as it may (a) have caused the original motor fault or (b) have been subsequently damaged by the motor failure.

INDUCTION MOTORS – CENTRIFUGAL START

A third system for induction motor starting may also be utilised although it is restricted to tumble dry only machines. It is used on some makes of machine both old and current. The stator, as before, is split into start and run windings. The start windings are connected in series with a micro-switch, the switching arm of which rests on a movable circular collar forming part of a spring and weight system fixed to the rotor shaft. When power is supplied to both windings of the motor, rotation is induced by the phase displacement of the two windings. **Note:** This may be increased further by the addition of a capacitor within the start winding supply.

As the rotor increases in speed, centrifugal force lifts the weights and the movement produced is used to pull the collar away from the micro-switch arm and in doing so, switches off the start windings. The motor continues to run with only the run windings in circuit.

Switching out the start windings in this way (centrifugal or relay start) greatly improves the efficiency of the motor and reduces any heat caused if the start winding imbalance were to be left in. Remember the imbalance is only there to

induce initial rotation. Once rotation is achieved they are in effect, no longer required for the motor to continue running.

In addition to the normal motor faults relating to capacitor (if fitted), worn bearings, faulty windings, etc., there are three further possible mechanical faults:

1. The micro-switch may fail in either the closed or open position. If permanently open circuit, the motor would over-heat when first turned on as only the run windings would receive power (but rotation would not occur). Should the micro-switch fail in the closed position, the motor would start. The collar and weights would move but the run windings would remain in circuit. This permanent imbalance would result in a slower speed than normal and over heating of the motor.

2. Failure of the centrifugal system to reset when the motor stops leaves the start windings open circuit and the fault will arise when the machine is next used. See No. 1 for fault symptoms.

3. The failure of the centrifugal system to move the collar from its rest position results in the start windings being left in circuit. See No. 1 for symptoms.

Faults 2 and 3 may be attributable to infrequent cleaning of the interior of the tumble dry only machine which would lead to fluff jamming the centrifugal mechanism.

Machines that use a centrifugal switch system can be identified by the distinct noise that the motor makes shortly after initial start up and just before stopping rotation when the motor is switched off. The noise (a faint whirr and click) is caused by the movement of the weights and collar and switch, both on initial run up to speed, i.e. switching out the start winding, and run down then the motor is turned off, i.e. resetting of weights, collar and switch.

Ensure all moving parts are securely fitted, clean and free to move. Do not over lubricate as this can itself cause a fluff build up. Apply a very small amount of light machine oil only to the moving parts of the mechanism.

INDUCTION MOTORS (SHADED POLE)

This type of motor is associated with pumps and low power air circulation fans, etc., as it has low starting torque, i.e. this style of motor is impeded from starting easily, as the initial rotation is only from copper segments bound into the stator. When power is applied to the stator coil, the copper segments create a permanent imbalance in the magnetic field produced. This induces rotational movement.

The shaded pole motor is one of the most simple of all induction motors and is similar in basic format of rotor and stator. However, only one stator coil is used to create the magnetic field. Obviously this alone would not induce rotation of the rotor, only a constant magnetic field. To start rotation, an imbalance in the magnetic field is required which is done quite simply by copper band inserts at the pole ends of the stator laminations. The copper bands within the mild steel stator laminations (dissimilar metals) distort the magnetic field in a given direction, therefore inducing rotation in the stator. Reversing the supply to such motors does not effect any change in motor direction as this is governed by the direction of the fixed shaded poles. These motors do not have a high starting torque and because of the magnetic imbalance being fixed, heating of the stator occurs which, under normal conditions creates no problems, but most stator coils are protected by T.O.C.s for safety.

Note: Connection can be reversed but direction of rotation remains the same. It is governed by the shaded poles only.

Typical shaded pole induction motor pump.

INDUCTION MOTORS (PERMANENT MAGNET ROTOR)

This extremely simple style of motor is used to drive all versions of mechanical timers, both for timing and cam advance. Consisting only of a wound circular coil fixed around a permanent magnet rotor and supported at both ends by simple sleeve bearings, this motor can be made extremely small and at a low cost. As with all induction motors, its simplicity of construction limits it for use to A.C. supply only. A larger version of this principle is now being used to power outlet pumps in many modern machines. The P.M. rotor is housed within a sealed plastic chamber, but is still free to

Component parts of a permanent magnet rotor pump. Only complete pumps are available if they fail in any way. It is shown here dismantled to illustrate its simplicity.

Small permanent magnet rotor type motors have been used for many years to drive mechanical timers.

rotate by the alternating current (A.C.) supplied to two externally mounted stator poles. The rotor drives the impeller of the pump in the normal way, only the motor of the pump differs.

This type of motor has been used for many years to power the timing and advance mechanism of washing machine programmers. As mentioned previously, some versions are now used to drive the outlet pump of some machines. It is the most simple of electric motors, quiet to run and cheap to produce. It also avoids some of the more common pump problems.

A circular multi-pole permanent magnet forms the rotor of the motor and its construction is similar to that described in the module control section relating to the tacho. Within the casing of timer motors a finely wound coil encased in plastic surrounds the permanent magnet rotor. Permanent magnet pumps have two coils wound on to a laminated steel stator. In both instances, supplying A.C. power to the coil(s) induces rotation of the magnetic rotor. However, rotation could start in either direction and this, in the case of timer motors, would be most unwelcome. To ensure that rotation occurs in the required direction, i.e. clockwise or counter clockwise, a small plastic cam is positioned within the casing (seen as a small plastic pip on the rear of the motor casing), which allows

rotation in one direction only. Should the motor try to start in the wrong direction, it hits the plastic cam which flicks it back, thus inducing correct rotation.

The ability to run in both directions is utilised to its full extent when this style of motor is used to drive an outlet pump impeller. Should the impeller of the pump come into contact with an item such as a button (this would normally jam/stall a normal shaded pole motor), the motor may be nudged into revolving in the opposite direction and clear the blockage or continue to pump whilst running in the opposite direction.

The construction of the p.m. pump helps alleviate the problem of shaft seal leaks and bearing failure which are common to shaded pole versions.

Failure other than brush wear requires complete motor renewal – make sure only the correct replacement is obtained.

ARMATURE CHANGE

The main aim of this photographic sequence is to show the removal of a motor from a machine and the detailed removal and refitting of a new armature and brush ring. This was possible in this instance as the individual motor parts were available.

The motor shown is of a universal type which is found in many early wash-only and vented washerdrier machines in the Hoover range. Later machines and condenser washerdrier types are more likely to have motors where only the motor brushes are available as replacement items. This practice is now common to a large proportion of machines from all manufacturers such as Creda, Ariston, Zanussi, Servis, Indesit, etc.

It must be remembered that any connections that are to be removed should first be noted to ensure correct refitting at the end of the repair.

Shown also is the brush replacement for the G.E.C. type motor, variations of which can be found in Hotpoint, Indesit and Creda machines. **Note:** Any other fault with this type of motor requires a complete change of unit.

Armature change – Hoover type model

1. Isolate the machine and remove the rear panel.

2. In this case a 'low insulation test' disclosed the motor fault. Remove the motor bolts and withdraw from the machine.

3. After noting the motor block colours, positions and connections, remove the plastic cover to reveal the tacho coil. The tacho coil and magnet can be removed carefully. (The clip on the shaft can be lifted with a small screwdriver).

4. The four end rivets can be drilled out or removed with a sharp chisel, as in this instance.

5. Mark the position of the end frames, by marking with a pencil. When marked, remove the four securing bolts.

7. Knock the armature tacho end shaft free. Remove armature and inspect for faults.

8. Check copper segments on armature for damage, i.e. burnt looking or loose/raised segments, and for carbon build-up. (This one is badly damaged).

9. Check the bearings for free and quiet running by spinning them on the shaft. Also check for tight fit to shaft. (This one had damaged the shaft).

6. When the end bolts are removed, use a hide mallet (or similar) to free and remove the front end frame.

10. *New armature ready to fit. Note screw plates and screws instead of rivets to aid fitting. Fit replacement unit if in any doubt as to condition of old unit.*

11. *Old brush ring inspected for damage. Carefully check for smooth brush slides. Also check that no carbon deposits have caused low insulation. Change if in any doubt. (This one has burnt slides).*

12. *Shown are new and old brushes. The top lines show tagged and non-tagged type of brushes. The lower lines show split and worn brushes.*

13. *New armature and brush ring fitted to rear end frame.*

14. Refit tacho magnet and clip. Ensure that when fitted the magnet will not turn on the shaft, i.e., it should be locked to the armature.

16. Refit front end frame and re-assemble motor, lining up the marks made in step 6.

15. Adjust tacho setting (if necessary). Screw centre up to the magnet and turn back 1½ turns only.

17. Fitting of new brushes. Ensure free movement of brush in slide. Make sure all connections are tight and do not foul metal body of motor.

Ensure insulation strip is fitted to brush opening. It will fit easily if warmed first. The motor is now ready to fit to the machine for function testing when all panels have been refitted.

GEC type motor (Fault example)

1. GEC type motor. Early type can now have similar armature change as Hoover type, but generally only brushes fitted.

2. Removal of brush and holder from GEC type motor. Insert screwdriver and lift tongue of plastic at base of holder.

3. Slide out brush holder complete with brush. Note length of new brush and check for good movement of brush in slide. This brush has worn very short.

4. View of new brush and holder complete. Early screw-on type brush holders have separate brushes as above.

5. Ensure that any carbon dust deposits inside motor casing and armature are removed. (Blow out dust and clean with pipe cleaner or similar). Take care, do not inhale the dust.

6. Refitting of GEC type brush holder and complete brush assembly. Slide back into position carefully ensuring that tongue of holder engages into position.

MODULE CONTROL FOR BRUSH MOTORS

It must be remembered that all motor speed faults are not directly attributable to the motor. The fault could be caused by a piece of electronics called a module which is connected between the timer and the motor and controls the speed of the motor. There is no standard location for the module but it is easily identified by its distinct printed circuit board (P.C.B.) and large heatsink. Computer controlled machines normally integrate the speed control into the power module, see Timers chapter. On the rear end of the motor's armature is a circular magnet that revolves in unison with it.

Close to this magnet is a coil of copper wire (this may be encased in plastic), which is called a tacho generator. If a magnet is rotated next to, or inside a coil of wire a current is produced which is proportional to the rotational speed of the magnet. Therefore, the faster the motor is running the more current is produced. This current is fed to the module as a reference voltage and is used to monitor the performance of the motor by comparing the relative speed of the motor with a known voltage via a comparator circuit. If the reference voltage is found to be lower than the comparator voltage, the module will increase the pulse rate, therefore increasing the speed of the motor. If the voltage is found to be high, the pulses are slowed, therefore decreasing the motor's speed. This happens many times a second, and is undetectable.

The reverse side of the PCB with the heat sink removed to show the components of the module clearly. The faulty components can be seen directly behind the area of discoloration. The component (a resistor in this case), has been overheating and subsequently failed. Repairs to modules are not merely a simple replacement of obvious components, as micro-chips within the circuit may have been damaged. We therefore advise that the module be removed and replaced with a complete new unit.

Shown is the module from a Hotpoint Automatic. Note the discoloration that has occurred on the centre of the PCB (front). This is a sure sign that the module is at fault or will fault soon.

The burnt connection on this Ariston washerdrier motor module was caused by a loose connection creating arcing and localised overheating.

HOW TO CHECK IF THE MODULE IS AT FAULT

Warning: The machine must be isolated from the mains. Turn off at the wall socket and remove the plug.

If any of the internal components of the module have burned out, i.e. charred or burnt looking, the motor should be checked for any shorting, loose wires or low resistance, as these may be the probable cause.

CHECKS ON THE TACHO MAGNET AND TACHO COIL

(a) If the magnet is loose or broken, this would result in incorrect speeds at lower motor speeds.

(b) Severe damage or complete loss of the magnet would cause the motor to spin on all positions.

(c) A break in the coil would result in a spin on all positions. This is because a 'good' coil is usually about 200 to 1600 ohms resistance. If there is a break in the coil, the resistance is 0 ohms. The tacho generator is not returning any current, therefore the module speeds the motor up. The increased speed is not transmitted back to the module, so the process is repeated _ad infinitum_.

Note: Most modules fitted to modern machines have an inbuilt tacho test circuit and will not operate if the tacho circuit is open.

(d) Breaks and/or poor connections of the wires leading to and from the tacho can have the same effect. This is especially true at the connection block with the motor, and the connection at the module.

It should be remembered that any loose connection will be aggravated by the movement of the tub on the suspension, and this should be taken into account when testing for such faults. The following chart can be used to help locate the module faults and show the correct course of action. Do not attempt to adjust the

Tacho generator.

		Interlock	Motor	Tacho	Module		Tacho	Timer
Check Operation		Check Interlock and Latch	Check Complete Motor Circuits	Check Circuit Late M/C's	Fit New One	Replace Original	Fit New One or Adjust	Check Timer moves on at all
Spin	None	●	●	●	●			
	Slow		●		●			
	Cont		●	●	●			●
Distribute	Cont	●	●	●	●			●
	None		●	●	●			
	Fast		●	●	●	●	●	
	Slow		●	●	●	●	●	
Tumble	None	●	●		●			
	Fast			●	●		●	
	Slow		●	●	●	●	●	
	Cont		●	●	●			●

Incorrect Drum Action

tachometer other than as shown in the armature section.

The modules shown are a small selection of modules that are fitted to today's machines. Their appearance and function differ very little from one another, but are strictly non-interchangeable. Always ensure that the correct replacement unit is obtained by quoting the make, model and serial number of your machine when ordering spare parts.

If the fault persists the module is probably at fault. This should be replaced with a new unit, ensuring that the correct type is purchased. To fit, make a note of the connections, remove them and replace them on the new unit. It is important that the 'Duotine' (edge) connector fits tightly on the module (the connections can be closed slightly by inserting a small screwdriver between the back of the tag and the plastic duotine. Care should be taken not to close it too far as this

may result in the tag not making contact by being pushed back into the connector).

The machine must be isolated from the mains. Turn off at the wall socket and remove the plug.

Warning: The large metal back of the module is used as a heatsink. This means that it is live when in use, and therefore should be fitted correctly and securely to its plastic mounts. Even when testing, any contact with the earthed shell of the machine will render the unit useless.

MODULE CONTROL INDUCTION MOTORS

Many modern machines that use induction motors now use electronics to help control the selected speed more precisely and help smooth the transition from one speed to another. They differ little from their predecessors and still require a complex set of windings within

the stator to give a series of fixed speeds. However, they do have the addition of further speed control via a speed control module and tacho coil and magnet arrangement which is similar to the system used to control brush motors.

Faults in either motor or module would require a complete change as no internal components are available, except for the tacho coil.

CENTRIFUGAL PULLEYS

The centrifugal or variomatic pulley is the large pulley that can be seen on some induction motors in such as the Candy, early Ariston, Indesit and Philips washerdriers.

WHAT DOES IT DO?

It is fitted to help increase the drum speed when the machine spins.

OPERATION OF A CENTRIFUGAL PULLEY SYSTEM

Small Belt Drive Point

Centrifugal Weights

SLOW MOTOR SPEEDS

Fixed Pulley Front

Larger Belt Drive Point

Sliding Rear of Pulley

FAST MOTOR SPEEDS (SPIN)

WHY HAVE COMPLEX PULLEYS?

The reason for having adjustable pulley drives relates mainly to the need for faster spinning at the end of the wash cycle. Adding a large pulley to the motor to create an increase in drive ratio to the drum pulley for the spin, causes problems. The low speed wash action would require extra windings to slow the rotation whilst high spin speeds would be affected by lack of torque as the number of poles are reduced to increase the motor speed. In the past when spin speeds were much slower (500–800 rpm) the induction motor was the ideal choice. However, the need for ever faster spin speeds has outstripped the capabilities of the normal induction motor. To compensate for this inability to comfortably reach higher drive speeds further mechanical additions have been made to the drive pulley and in some instances (Candy) to both drive and drum pulley. Some Zanussi machines use a gear and clutch arrangement to help in increasing the drive speed of their induction motor. Both of these systems are still limited to a drive ratio that produces a maximum spin speed of 1000 rpm (of the drum).

Universal brush motors are required for machines with spin speeds that exceed 1000 rpm (many modern machines now attain 1400 rpm).

HOW DOES IT WORK?

Weights within the pulley are pushed outwards by centrifugal force when a fast motor speed is selected. As the pulley is constructed in two halves, the outward movement narrows the gap between the front and back plate of the pulley, therefore increasing its diameter.

This increase in diameter increases the drive ratio between the drum pulley and the motor pulley. When the motor speed allows, the reverse occurs, i.e. the back plate moves away from the front plate, and the belt rides on the smaller diameter of the pulley.

Similar clutches can be found on Ariston and Philips machines. Candy machines also have a similar centrifugal pulley on the drum, although this opens at the higher speeds, thus giving a smaller drive ratio. This produces an increase in speed with a constant belt tension, without having to resort to expensive motor windings. **Do not** overtighten the drive belt on machines with a centrifugal pulley. **Note:** Some are self-tensioning by the weight of the motor, i.e. motor only supported by rubber mounts on the rear end frame, allowing the weight of the motor to tension the belt and the motor to rise as the pulley size and drive increases during the spin.

The addition of a mechanical pulley system to an otherwise simple and reliable motor increases the risk of faults. In addition to the normal induction motor faults, problems occur with the mechanical action of both centrifugal motor pulleys and drum pulleys (if fitted). Due to the belt being constantly squeezed along its edges, belt wear is accelerated and regular checks are advised. Renew if suspect as spin efficiency will decrease and/or excessive noise will occur.

Pulleys are made either of plastic or cast aluminium and as such, wear ridges form on the

This large induction motor with centrifugal pulley is supported only by the large rubber mounts to the rear of the motor. This allows the weight of the motor to self tension the drive belt and to rise and fall as the pulley increases and decreases in diameter with speed. Increased belt wear is common with this system.

belt contact faces. This may lead to restricted movement of the belt resulting in poor drive (poor wash, spin or both), noise, excessive belt wear or jamming and finally, possible motor failure.

The Zanussi geared systems are similar, with noise and internal gear wear being the most common problems. There are no individual spare parts available for these types of drive pulleys, therefore if faults do occur, complete pulleys will be required. However, it is not uncommon for some manufacturers to supply the pulley and motor as one unit, no matter what the fault.

Geared clutch drive as used on some Zanussi induction motors.

Chapter 28

Belts

The main drive belts used in both automatic washing machines (wash only and combined washerdrier versions) and dry-only machines are of two distinctly different types. Both kinds are found in a multitude of size variations, but each machine must be correctly fitted with the exact size and type and no other. The two types of belt are, the VEE, so called because of its location on 'V' shaped pulleys, and MULTI 'V' belts which are much flatter and have a series of 'V' formations on the drive face. The use of a multi 'V' formation gives a greater contact surface area in relation to the belt width. This is necessary as the belt is designed to be driven by a much smaller and therefore faster rotating drive pulley than the larger single 'V' drive pulleys.

In general 'V' belts are to be found on washing machines with induction motors and multi 'V' belts are found on washing machines with brush gear motors of all types. Tumble dry only machines in the main use multi 'V' belts (of a smaller width and fewer Vs) to rotate the main drum via an induction motor. However, a combination of multi 'V' and 'V' belts can be found on some early tumbledriers such as Burco and Hotpoint. It is also possible to encounter an elasticated belt on

A. B. and C. are multi 'V' belt variations. A. is predominantly used in tumble dry only machines whereas A. B. and C. are found in both wash only and combined machines.
D. depicts the profile of a 'V' belt and can be found in wash only, combined and tumble dry only machines.
E. is a cross section of an elasticated belt restricted to use in certain tumble dry only machines.

Typical simple 'V' belt drive. Belt tension is by motor adjustment.

some tumble dry only machines which is used to drive the independent fan unit. Machines such as Candy, Hoover and Burco appliances can be found with this configuration, See Dry only machines chapter.

Double jockey pulley system required for reversing tumble dry only machines.

WHAT ARE 'V' BELTS MADE OF?

Both types of belt consist of woven nylon cords upon which a synthetic rubber is moulded. The single 'V' belt has sides of approximately 40 degrees and terminating in a flat base. The Multi 'V' belt is a series of peaks and troughs, the number of which varies with the work load requirements of the belt. Always ensure that a replacement belt is the correct size and width. Most belts have sizes or size codes printed on the outer face. However, such marks are often illegible on old belts due to wear. Take a note of the make, model and serial number of your machine along with any legible belt code when obtaining a replacement belt.

Typical jockey pulley components and configuration. Note: most but not all belts will be tensioned as depicted in the two diagrams. Before removing the old belt make a note of the correct position of your machine as some of the alternative methods of tensioning are not so obvious.
A. Main drum drive belt multi 'V'.
B. Jockey pulley.
C. Pulley shaft.
D. Tensioning arm.
E. Multi 'V' drive pulley on motor shaft.
F. Pivot point.
G. Tension spring.

REMOVAL AND RENEWAL

The single 'V' belt drive system requires both drive pulley (the one on the motor) and drum pulley (the larger one on the drum shaft), to have a recessed groove the same dimensions as the belt. Multi 'V' systems can have two variations:

1. Both drive pulley and drum pulley are grooved to accept the Multi 'V' configuration of the belt.
2. Only the drive pulley is grooved (to aid grip on its much smaller surface area) and the drum pulley is smooth and slightly convex in shape. Grip is created on the drum pulley purely by it having a greater contact area to the belt when in use even though this is only on the peaks of the belt. The convex shape keeps the belt in place on the grooveless pulley and reduces wear if misalignment occurs. A similar system is used in tumble dry only machines where the belt runs directly on the outer of the drum, the size of which gives a much greater surface area and, due to its width allows the belt position to line up with both drive pulley and tension wheel.

BELT CARE

Ensure pulleys are in good condition, i.e. not chipped or buckled, etc., and are aligned correctly. Misalignment will shorten the working life of both types of belt. Poorly aligned belts will shed the rubber compound coating from the cords leaving tell tale dust or flakes in the base and surrounding area of the machine. This may block the 'V' section of multi 'V' belts and cause the belt to fly off usually on a spin cycle. Single 'V' belts may twist within the 'V' section when misaligned. Close inspection of belts is essential and reversing the belt and bending it is the

Turn belts inside out to check for problems. Do this over the whole length of the belt. This belt has detached outer cover and cracked inner wedge. A fault such as this requires renewal of the belt.

best way to inspect them. Check the whole length in this way. If any defects are found, renew the belt.

When removing a belt for inspection or during repair, care must be exercised to avoid damage to the belt itself. Do not use screwdrivers or similar to prise belts on or off as this can easily damage the belt cords and moulding of the soft aluminium pulleys used on washing machines. Slacken off the motor bolts to reduce tension (on washing machines) and pull the belt towards you midway between the pulleys whilst carefully rotating the drum pulley slowly clockwise. This will allow the belt to smoothly ride out of position. Reverse this process for refitting. **Note**: It is advisable to use protective gloves as the pulleys on machines can have very sharp edges.

BELT TENSION

It is natural for some degree of stretching and wear to occur during use which will result in the need for re-tensioning. Some machines may be self-tensioning, i.e. the weight of the motor keeps the belt under

tension (this system was popular with some early washerdriers). On most tumble dry only machines, a spring tension jockey pulley (so called as it rides on the belt) is used to keep the belt under tension. **Note**: two may be found on reversing tumbledriers. However the majority of washing machines and washerdriers rely on motor adjustment, i.e. two fixed bolts and one slotted, to tension the belt.

Setting the correct tension is essential. Too tight will quickly wear the belt and worse still, it will damage the drive pulley and cause premature motor bearing failure. Too slack and belt slip will occur resulting in poor wash, excessive vibration or heating of the belt which will result in belt damage or failure. On machines with aluminium pulleys, slipping can create ridges on the pulley grooves. If this does happen, the damaged pulley/pulleys will need renewing as any new belt fitted to such a pulley will soon become damaged by the uneven pulley surface.

The correct tension of a belt depends on its free distance between pulley contact points. As a rule a 12 mm deflection per 30 cm of free belt is required. Most washing machines have in the region of 30 cm of free belt between pulleys and therefore a 12 to 13 mm deflection is optimum. When fitted and tensioned correctly the belt will have a springy feel. Some stretching will occur to new belts, but modern good quality belts are much less affected. However, the belt will need to be checked at a later date and re-adjusted if required. Do not over tension a new belt in the misguided hope that this will overcome any initial stretching that may occur.

POINTS TO NOTE

It is not uncommon for belts to be warm after use even when correctly tensioned. This is due to the energy absorbed as the belt flexes and is proportional to the load. If the belt is hot or very warm after use, this would indicate incorrect tension or overloading causing belt slip and friction heating. Correct the problem, but check the belt for any cracking caused by overheating. If in doubt, renew the belt.

NOISE

This is usually a squealing type of noise most often heard on wash rotation and prior to spin (distribute) when the belt is under most load. This may simply be incorrect belt tension, slack, or worn pulleys, ridges on the pulleys, misaligned belt or machine overloaded. Again, isolate and correct fault and inspect belt closely for damage. If in doubt, renew it.

Ensure multi 'V' belts align correctly if both drive and drum pulley are grooved, note position of original belt, i.e. first groove on drive pulley is used then first groove on drum pulley is used. Misalignment of multi 'V' belts is easily done, so ensure that they are correctly fitted to avoid premature belt wear or the belt flying off during spin or wash cycles.

Machines with centrifugal clutch systems, See: Motors chapter, create quicker belt wear due to the constant squeezing and movement of the belt. Check the drive pulley closely for wear ridges and be prepared to change belts more frequently on this type of drive system to maintain peak performance.

Chapter 29
Suppressors

A suppressor is a device designed to eliminate the formation and transmission of spurious radio waves that may be produced by the operation of the motor and switches within the appliance during normal operation. When switching occurs within the appliance and it is not suppressed, small sparks at the contact points or brushes may produce interference on radio and T.V.

In line suppressor 4TAG type (variations possible).

Typical 'choke' suppressors.

In line suppressor flying load type (variations possible).

New style square suppressor.

channels or audio equipment plugged into the same electrical circuit, i.e. not only through air waves but also down the mains cable.

WHY SHOULD ALL APPLIANCES HAVE THEM?

By law, all domestic appliances must be suppressed to conform to the regulations on radio interference, and it is an offence to use an appliance that is not suppressed to these standards.

WHERE ARE THEY LOCATED?

Suppressors vary in style, shape, position, size and colour. Sometimes individual parts are suppressed but more often the mains supply is suppressed, but more often the mains supply is suppressed at or just after the entry point into the appliance. This is called 'in-line' suppression as both the live and neutral supply goes through the suppressor and on to supply the whole of the appliance with power. Do not confuse the suppressors with capacitors which may be used in the appliance for induction motor starting. They may look very similar but carry out distinctly different functions. Suppressors may also be called 'mains filters' because of their ability to remove spurious radio transmissions.

A revised version of suppression unit can be found in addition to those described above. This is an induction coil, fitted in series between the neutral position at the terminal block and the shell of the machine. As an induction coil is of a far heavier gauge, it only passes suppression current, whereas the two earlier versions carry the full voltage load. Some machines have a combination of both in-line and induction coil types of suppressor. All versions require a good earth path of both plug and socket, see Basics – electrical.

FAULTS WITH SUPPRESSORS (FILTERS)

The main fault is one of short circuit to earth usually resulting in the unit 'blowing' both the main fuse and itself. This is often accompanied by a pungent burnt smell. Renewal is a straightforward one for one replacement.

Open circuit problems can occur and the unit will fail to allow current to pass through as normal. The suppressor can easily be checked for continuity using a meter, see Using a meter chapter. When checking,

inspect the top insulation closely and if cracked or at all suspect, renew complete unit.

It is common for in-line suppressors to use the earth path as part of their filtering circuit (although very little power passes through it). It is essential for all appliances to have a good earth path. If an appliance with an in-line suppressor/filter has a break in its earth path (due to cable, plug or socket fault) small electric shocks may be experienced when the user touches metal parts of the appliance, especially if they are in touch with a good earth path themselves, e.g. holding metal sink or work top, etc. It is essential that such faults are traced and corrected immediately, see General safety guide and Basics chapters.

Although the continuity of a suppressor (lead through type) can be checked easily, its function of suppression cannot be so easily checked. If all other checks, i.e. good earth connection (check for loose/poor

connection to shell of machine), no cracks or loose/heated terminals, etc., prove to be OK, and interference to other equipment persists, renew the suppressor.

An additional means of suppression may be found, especially on micro-processor controlled machines. This is a choke type and may be fitted in series between live and neutral positions or individually in-line on both live and neutral supplies to individual components. Such units consist of a ferrite core or ring around which the conductor is wound.

Some appliances use a combination of different types of suppressor. Suppressors of any type should not be by-passed or omitted, as to have an unsuppressed appliance is an offence owing to the interference that it may cause to others, and in the case of 'chokes', failure or omission of this device may cause damage to or corrupt electronic circuits within the appliance, see Timers chapter.

Some suppressors give clear indication of failure.

Check suppression units closely for cracks or expansion, etc. If in doubt, renew it. This unit has a small crack across the top but otherwise it looks OK. However, internally it is a direct short circuit and potentially dangerous.

Chapter 30

Bearings

This chapter deals predominantly with the main drum support bearings, although many of the associated problems also relate to other areas such as main motor bearings on both washing machines and tumble dry only machines, and also fan and pump motors on machines which use ball race or roller bearings in these items. For items which contain sleeve bearings, see Pumps and Motors chapters, and for tumbledrier drum bearing variations, see the section which deals specifically with tumble dry only machines in conjunction with information from this chapter.

TYPES OF BEARING

Basically, there are three types of bearing used in washing machines and combined washerdriers:
1. The sleeve bearing. This is simply a phosphor bronze bush in which the motor shaft is free to rotate. It is more commonly used in pump and fan motors and reference to these sections will give further detail.
2. Ball race bearing. This type of bearing consists of an outer ring in which a small inner ring is supported by circular ball bearings and is free to rotate.
3. Taper roller bearing. The taper roller bearing uses rollers in place of the ball bearing in (2) and as its name implies, the

design angles the rollers to give a tapered appearance. The outer ring (shell) is not fixed as with the ball race type, and is fitted into position separately. It is essential that taper bearings are fitted as a matched pair, i.e. inner and outer. If this is not done, then the result will be early failure.

The type of bearings used on the main drum bearing assembly will differ not only between manufacturers, but also between

Typical ball race bearings open on the left and shielded on the right.

Top view of this Zanussi washerdrier shows that for drum renewal, it is necessary to remove the outer tub unit from the machine. This is due to only the front section of the outer tub being removable, see clamp bolt arrowed. However, bearing renewal can be carried out without outer tub removal.

models from one manufacturer, i.e. one range may use ball race bearings when a similar model from the same manufacturer will have taper roller bearings. Although there are only two types of bearing used, the variations in size of both outer and inner are vast, so therefore it is essential to fit identical bearings when replacing old or damaged ones and ensure that all shaft seals and spacers are renewed at the same time. If possible, obtain a bearing kit to make sure that all relevant parts are renewed. Do not cut corners by replacing only one bearing in a set of two or fitting a new taper roller inner to an existing outer shell because the old outer shell is difficult to remove. These short cuts will lead to premature failure and further damage. Be warned!

WHY DO BEARINGS FAIL?

There are several reasons why bearings fail apart from the normal wear and tear over a long period of time. What follows is a list of the most common causes and points to watch out for.

(a) The most common failure of both ball and taper bearings is the ingression of water and detergent into the bearing housing. This is usually due to wear or premature failure of the shaft seal. Two types of seal are used. The first one is a simple shaft seal which is pressed into the bearing housing on top of the front bearing. When assembled, the lower section of the drum shaft locates within the seal, usually a raised metal shoulder or collar of mild steel or more commonly phosphor bronze, and is fixed to the base of the drum shaft.

The seal has either one or two spring loaded lips which press firmly around the collar to create a watertight seal. Normal wear, fluff or scale may break

Illustrates scoured shaft.

Highlights how the bearing rests on a scoured shaft.

this seal down and allow water and detergent into the bearings quickly resulting in failure. Ensure that the collar is secure on the shaft and clean and that both seal and bearings are renewed at the same time. The second type of seal is a carbon face seal. This system relies on two smooth faces of carbon (or ceramic) that are pressed firmly together when assembled. One face is free to rotate, being fixed to the base of the drum shaft, whereas the other, as before, is fixed on top of the front bearing and is spring-loaded. The two smooth surfaces held under the pressure of the spring within the seal creates the movable watertight seal. Again, fluff, scale and normal wear will lead to water ingression.

Ensure that the fixed carbon ring is smooth, not cracked and securely fixed to the base of the shaft. Check the new spring-loaded face seal in a similar way and make sure that it seats correctly into the bearing housing. Application of a little sealant is recommended to make certain of a water-tight fit to the housing. Do not allow any sealant or dirt on either of the faces of the seals when assembling them.

(b) Bearings will also fail if incorrectly fitted. Do not hammer in the bearing (or shell, if taper roller type) directly with a hammer as this may crack or chip it. Do not force the bearing or shell into distorted or dirty housings as this will distort the bearing and create overheating resulting in failure. Inspect the drum shaft closely for ridges or rust which again will distort the inner race of the bearing, resulting in overheat or if worn, create a loose fit. Take care to clean all areas and fit only the correct size of bearings carefully. (c) Inspect failed bearings closely for they will have sizes stamped on them which can be used to ensure the new bearing is of the same dimensions. Failed bearings may also give an indication as to why they failed. Rust would indicate that the seal had failed and prompt closer inspection, cleaning or renewal of the shaft, collar or carbon face. Bearings that are dark blue or black in colour are usually the result of overheating. Check shape of housing and shaft and do not over grease. Flakes of metal from the bearing also indicate some form of distortion or ingress of dirt during assembly.

(d) Do not over tighten bearings (especially taper roller types) hoping that it will help seating. The result is usually overheating and premature failure.

RECOGNISING BEARING FAILURE

Noise can be a good guide to early recognition of bearing problems. Simply removing the drive belt should help ascertain if the faulty bearing is in the motor or the drum shaft support bearings. A selection of noise faults are given below along with possible causes.

Noises	Possible cause
Loud rumbling especially on spin	Collapsed front drum bearing or seized front bearing. This often results in shaft damage if not attended to quickly
Rattling with intermittent knocking	Ball or roller of bearing defective
Rattling/knocking proportional to speed	Inner or outer of bearing faulty
High pitched metallic noise	Common on worn motor bearings at high speed and on new bearing if it has been forced on to a damaged or over-sized shaft
High pitched ringing noise	Indication that bearing has been fitted to a damaged housing or fitted carelessly
Grating and crunching noise	Collapsed bearing cage or dirt between inner and outer race
Squeaking	On old bearing, usually due to lack of lubrication or ingress of water past shaft seal
	May also occur when new bearings are fitted to machine with carbon face type seals if care was not taken to keep both surfaces clean or if check was not carried out for cracks or scouring on carbon faces

TIPS ON FITTING

To gain maximum life from any bearing, care must be exercised when handling and fitting it. Prior to stripdown and removal of the old bearings, ensure that a note/drawing is made of the position of seals, clips and washers etc. Inspect both the shaft and housing closely for defects. Ensure the shaft, housing, work area and hands are clean. Remove the new bearing from its protective packaging only when you are ready to fit it.

Ideally, bearings should be pressed into position but in reality, however, this is not always possible and some means of drifting the bearing into place will be required. Great care must be taken if this method is used as damage can easily be done to the bearing at this stage. Endeavour to use a tube when fitting the bearing to enable an equal force to be applied. The tight fitting part of the bearing should take the force only, i.e. if fitting to a shaft, contact should only be with the inner race and when fitting a bearing into a housing, only the outer race should take the force. Do not apply any force to the part of the bearing that is free to rotate during fitting. To assist in fitting bearings, expansion and contraction with heat can be used although excessive heat must be avoided.

Fitting a bearing or taper roller bearing outer shell into its housing can be assisted by simply putting the bearing or shell into the household freezer for a while and warming the housing with the aid of a light bulb for an hour. This simple technique can help enormously. When fitting a bearing to a shaft, a reversal is required. Cool the shaft and warm the bearing, but be careful not to overheat the bearing (especially sealed bearings) as this may create

Position 1. shows a bearing that is incorrectly positioned and is proud of its correct location point. Position 2. indicates the collar on which the shaft seal will ride. Ensure it is both clean and secure.

Do not fit a bearing in this manner as damage to the bearing can easily be caused.

problems. Do not exceed 100 degrees C.

Many ball type bearings are greased during manufacture and sealed on both sides. Such bearings do not require any extra lubrication prior to assembly. Roller bearings (and some open cage ball bearings) do require packing with grease. This should be done sparingly as over greasing results in churning of the grease and heating takes place which results in loss of lubrication. Pack the bearing with grease and rotate both inner and outer with the fingers to allow any excess to be pushed out from the moving parts.

Press the bearing home, ideally by using a bearing press tube and metal plate. However, if access to a press is not possible, carefully use a hammer in its place after first applying heat as described in the text. An alternative method is to use two large metal plates/washers and a long bolt and nut to press the bearings into position by tightening the nut and bolt.

TYPICAL TAPERED BEARING CHANGE

The following sequence of pictures shows the renewal of a set of drum bearings. In this particular machine, the main drum support bearings were found to be worn and water damaged. This has been caused by the carbon seal failing and allowing water and detergent to enter the bearing and housing.

This was suspected because of the noise of the machine especially on spin, and confirmed by removing the drive

Metal tube

Metal plate

belt from the motor to the drum pulley, spinning the drum slightly by hand and listening for any grating noise. If this had been quiet, the motor would have been spun in the same way to test its bearings.

To confirm the drum bearing fault, another simpler method is to open the door of the machine and move the bottom of the door seal in order to see the inner drum and outer tub gap clearly, then try to lift the top lip only of the drum. At this point, the gap between the outer tub and inner drum should neither increase or decrease in size and no movement other than that of the outer tub on its suspension should be felt. This applies to all machines irrespective of bearing types. Picture 12 shows that the drum and spider mount was breaking loose from its position on the drum, due to a form of metal fatigue fracturing the drum. The only possible cure for the fracture, was the fitting of a complete new drum assembly. The initial fault was also rectified, being a renewal of the bearings. The user was unfortunate in needing the drum unit, especially when the support shaft itself was in such good condition.

The removal of the drum and backhalf assembly on this style of machine is quite straightforward. This style of drum and backhalf are fitted to many of the leading makes including Hoover, early Hotpoint, Creda and Servis, although in each case the size of bearing and type of seal differ slightly between machines. As the bearing kits are complete matched sets, no problems should arise.

After isolating the machine and laying it face down on a suitable surface, the removal of the backpanel in this instance revealed the backhalf and outer securing nuts. All of the nuts and bolts securing the backhalf and tub should be removed. If

necessary the top of the machine may be removed to gain access to the top bolts.

When this is done, mark all of the connections to the heater and thermostat and disconnect them. The back half assembly can now be manoeuvred from its position and removed from the back of the machine. The backhalf is made watertight by a rubber seal located on its outer edge. If the backhalf sticks to the tub, removal all the necessary nuts and bolts and gently prise the back half from the tub (do not use excessive force). The drum and backhalf can now be manoeuvred free of the machine. The removal of the pulley and bearings can now proceed.

If the bearing set for your machine is of the ordinary ball bearing type, the job is much easier as the old bearing should knock out in one piece. Should this type of bearing 'collapse' or leave its outer shell, the shell can be removed as shown as for the taper bearing shell in picture 18. Care must be taken not to go too deep with the drill into the soft aluminium housing.

When greasing the new bearing (this is obviously not necessary on the sealed bearing type) take care not to over-grease them, as this will not help lubricate it and in fact will considerably reduce the bearing life.

The new taper bearing kit will come complete with an odd shaped aluminium washer that fits between the rear bearing spacer and pulley. This is known as a torque washer and is essential for the correct operation of the taper roller bearings. Always fit a new torque washer to this type of bearing system if the pulley is removed for any reason. Do not use the old one. The torque washer is a simple way of putting the taper bearings under a known pressure without the use of a torque wrench.

When fitted together, the

torque washer collapses at a given pressure and dispenses with the need for a torque wrench for tightening the pulley bolt.

A full set of instructions for the torque washer should come with the new bearing kit, however a typical taper bearing change sequence is as follows.

If your machine has ball bearings, please disregard the paragraph concerning torque washers, as that type of bearing assembly does not require a torque setting. Renewal of this type of bearing is a simple reversal of the strip-down procedure.

INSTRUCTIONS FOR BEARING CHANGE

1. How to dismantle the old pulley and bearings.
(i) Remove the bolt (1) and washer (2 & 3) securing the tub pulley and remove the pulley (4).
(ii) When removing the backhalf gasket, you will notice that it is compressed. It is advisable to replace this item to ensure a true water-tight seal between the backhalf housing and outer tub.
2. Extraction of old bearings.
(i) The existing bearing sleeves (9 & 11) will be found inside the tub backplate (10). Extract the bearing sub assemblies and then apply heat to the area containing the sleeves. The sleeves can then be gently tapped out with a small chisel, drift or screwdriver.
3. Renewal of bearings.
(i) Push the new sleeves into place, ensuring that the inner surface of the tub backplate is thoroughly cleaned.
(ii) Insert the first (larger) bearing and washer (12).
(iii) Gently push the seal (13) into place. It is advisable to use a waterproof adhesive around the seal to aid fitting and prevent leaking past the outer edge.
(iv) Clean the new carbon face

seal thoroughly to remove all traces of grease, oil, etc.

(v) It is advisable to fit new washers to the front and rear (12 & 7) as it is likely they have been scoured by the faulty bearings. Many bearing kits do not contain items 12 & 7 and these may have to be obtained separately.

(vi) With the drum face down, fit the backhalf with the new front bearing spacer and carbon seal fitted, to the cleaned and inspected drum and shaft.

(vii) The rear bearing race can now be fitted.

4. Inserting the torque washer.

(i) Re-assemble the remaining parts in reverse order to that in which they were removed. Do not use the old torque washer (6) – only use the new spacer supplied with the kit.

(ii) Fit the shim washer from the kit under the torque washer. In the position shown in (6A).

(iii) Tighten the bolt (1) against the pulley as far as possible without locking the tab washer.

(iv) Complete the tightening operation until the 'D' washer fits firmly against the shoulder of the spider unit (5).

(v) The spacer is now correctly pre-set. It is essential to do this, in order to ensure the correct loading pressure on the bearings.

5. Discard shim and complete re-assembly.

(i) Remove the bolt (1), washers (2 & 3), pulley (4) and spacer (6). Discard the shim (6A).

(ii) Re-assemble in reverse order again. This time locking the tab washer against the bolt.

(iii) If this procedure on taper roller bearings is not followed correctly, the life of the new bearing set could be considerably shortened.

Below are a few helpful hints on the refitting of the assembly back in the machine.

(a) It is advisable to remove the heater from the back half before refitting the back half and drum into the machine. The subsequent refitting of the heater in this fashion ensures the correct location of the internal heater securing clip, see Heaters chapter.

(b) A thermostat pod (if applicable) and the heater grommet can be helped by a smear of sealant to help slide them into position. If the thermostat grommet looks perished, it should be changed.

(c) Remember to reseal any hoses on the pressure system if they have been disturbed.

(d) Always remember to fit a new tub back half seal.

(e) Check the tension on the main drive belt and adjust the belt if necessary. This is done by moving the motor up or down to slacken or tighten the belt (like adjusting a fan belt on a motor car). Do not over-tighten the belt, see Belts chapter.

(f) Many condenser washerdriers will have connections to the back half. There are numerous variations of fixings but correct and secure fixing is common to all. Ensure all connections are tight. Any damaged clips should be renewed along with any sealant used at connection points etc.

1	Bolt	7	Washer (thin)
2	Locking washer	8	Small bearing
3	Washer (small)	9	Bearing sleeve
4	Pulley	10	Tub backplate
5	'D' washer	11	Bearing sleeve
6	Spacer	12	Washer (thick)
6a	Shim (disposable)	13	Carbon face seal

1. Isolate the machine and remove the rear panel. Note all connections to the back plate.

3. Note the position and angle of pressure vessel and remove.

2. Protect the face of the machine and gently lay the machine on its front.

4. Note connections on the thermostat. Remove thermostat with the wires still connected. Use a flat bladed screwdriver to ease it from the seal.

5. Having noted the wiring connections, they can now be removed. Slacken the heater clamp nut and gently prise the heater free.

6. Remove the back half bolts from around the perimeter of the tub.

7. The discharge from the drain hole can be seen here, and indicates water penetration of the bearings. The discharge is a mixture of grease, rust and water.

9. With drum and bearing unit completely removed from the machine it is much easier to work on.

10. Unlock the tab on the pulley bolt with the aid of a flat bladed screwdriver.

11. Remove the pulley bolt, pulley and spacers, etc., noting their correct order.

8. With all fixing bolts removed and wires secured out of the way, the drum and back half can be manoeuvred free from the tub.

14. (see photo 12) Check the three mounting points for cracks, etc. This drum and shaft are crush bolt fitted, therefore any fault on the drum or shaft requires a complete drum. Not all machines have this system.

17. With rear bearing removed, knock our rear bearing shell/liner by the inner lip.

12. Backplate freed from the drum shaft. (The front bearing may seize on the shaft and will have to be drawn off with pullers. If this happens, protect the shaft end by refitting the bolt onto the end of the shaft. This protects the shaft and aids the location of the puller centre).

15. Insert screwdriver and prise out bearing carbon face seal.

18. If there is no visible lip to the front bearing shell, drill two slots opposing each other in the inner of the housing to expose the liner. Do not drill too deeply.

13. Check shaft carefully for wear and ridges at the bearing support points. (Front and rear). Also check carbon face for cracks or loose fit. The example shown is OK.

16. Remove old washer and front bearings. In this case a taper bearing was found. Ball bearings will have to be knocked out with a metal drift.

19. Position of drill mark on front inner.

20. Remove the old thermostat seal if it is found to be a poor fit, or perished. Apply sealant to the new seal to ensure a good watertight seal.

21. Clean all seal and bearing surfaces prior to refitting new parts.

22. New set of taper roller bearings, torque washer and carbon seal suitable for this machine.

23. Typical set of ball bearings. Seals and bearing sizes may differ. Not interchangeable with taper bearings, not suitable for this machine.

24. Insert rear bearing liner and tap into position firmly, seating to its base using a soft metal drift.

25. Now insert front liner and repeat operation as in step 24.

26. Grease bearings back and front and re-assemble as described in text.

29. Tighten the bolts in sequence slowly using opposing bolts. Do not overtighten.

27. Back half ready to be fitted to the drum shaft.

30. Seal and refit all hoses and grommets and secure all connections to the heater, etc. Adjust the belt tension prior to the functional test with all panels in position.

28. Following the instructions for use of torque washer and shim, the unit is made ready for fitting back into the machine. Make sure that you reset the lock tab on the pulley bolt.

1. With machine isolated, open door and remove the securing screws for the plastic surround for the door seal.

3. Free the door seal from the outer shell lip of the machine and allow to rest on inside of the front panel.

2. Next, remove the door seal surround carefully. This is in two halves (top and bottom).

4. Remove the screws holding the timer knob in position. On early models, only one plastic screw will be found.

5. Pull to remove the soap drawer and remove the exposed screws. This allows the front facia to be removed.

6. Remove the screws securing the top of the front panel.

7. Remove the screws securing the bottom of the front panel. Hexagonal headed bolts may be found on early models.

10. With the clips removed, the tub front can be removed completely. Take care not to damage heater or connections.

11. Remove the screws securing the rear panel to expose the drum pulley.

8. With front panel off, remove the door catch and interlock (if fitted).

9. Note the position of the clips securing the front of the outer tub and remove carefully.

12. Remove the pulley lock nut (right hand thread) and 'chock' the pulley against the tub with a wedge of wood.

13. With the pulley securely wedged, grasp inner paddles of the drum and turn anti-clockwise. This will unscrew the pulley.

14. With pulley removed, tap the drum shaft free from the bearings using a soft-headed mallet.

15. Withdraw the drum and shaft from the tub. This will allow ample room to 'drift' out the ball bearings and shaft seal. Bearing replacement for this type of drum is quite straight-forward. Using a soft drift, knock the new bearing home, taking care not to damage the new seal. Re-assembly of your machine is a reversal of the previous procedure.

16. This machine also had severe drum damage as indicated.

17. This style of machine has a 'catch pot' style filter in the sump hose. When removed a large amount of coins, metal screws, curtain hooks and various other household items were found.

18. These items should not have been allowed to enter the machine. They have damaged the drum severely. What would have been a relatively inexpensive 'bearing only' repair, has now required the renewal of a costly drum. (The £1.44 that was found did not cover the cost of the new drum!). This could have been avoided with a little care and attention to pockets, etc., when loading the machine.

BEARING CHANGES NEEDING TUB REMOVAL

Often, the restricted rear access or reverse tub construction will not allow for the renewal of the bearings or drum in the manner previously described. In such instances, for repairs to or renewal of the drum bearings, tub seals or outer or inner drum renewal it may be necessary for the whole of the outer and inner drum unit to be removed from the shell of the machine before further stripdown can take place. There are two main reasons why this course of action may be required:

1. Access to the rear of the outer tub is restricted because of the very small access panel on the rear of the shell of the machine. However, on machines with external cast iron bearing holders, it is usually possible to manoeuvre the whole unit out through the opening after first laying the machine face down and removing the securing bolts and pulley. Several Zanussi and Ariston models can have bearings fitted in this way but for inner drum removal/renewal, the whole unit would need to be removed as described, see below.

2. The construction of the outer tub is jointed at the front of the machine and not the rear as is usual in most machines, and the inner drum can only be removed by first removing the front of the outer tub (unfortunately, in most instances the front shell of the machine is not removable and so the whole unit needs to be removed as described).

Most models in the Candy range of machines require tub unit removal for both bearing or drum problems.

It is not uncommon for manufacturers to buy-in products from another manufacturer and then 'badge' it as their own. This leads to a mix of model designs throughout the range. Until fairly recently, the current production machines were merely updated variations on a basic design, and therefore some continuity and standard format existed. However, this is not always the case nowadays which means that each machine has to be assessed prior to carrying out repairs, e.g. are the bearings mounted in a detachable housing? If access requires removal of the front of outer tub, can the front of the machine be removed to allow main unit to remain *in situ*? (see – Hotpoint photo sequence).

If no other option exists, the outer tub unit complete with drum and bearing will have to be removed to allow for complete stripdown. The removal of this large unit is via the top of the machine shell. The following text describes the removal of the outer tub unit after removing such items as the top/bottom tub weights, pulley, all connections and hoses and electrical connections to the unit. A photo sequence is not used for this as it would tend to mislead rather than help as each machine will have distinct variations depending on the original manufacturer.

It is advisable to remove all knobs from the front of the machine to reveal the fixing screws of the items behind them when servicing the drum, bearings, outer tub and seals which entails the removal of the outer tub unit from the machine via the top of the machine's cabinet as a complete unit. These should be unscrewed and the components laid over the front facia of the machine. If possible do not disconnect any wiring, but detailed notes of all connections and fixings should be kept in the event of items getting misplaced or dislodged. Release the screws securing the dispenser unit to the cabinet and remove the hose from the dispenser unit. Lay the dispenser unit over the front of the machine. Remove the top tub weight (if fitted) and release the front fitting of the door seal. To help slide the tub unit out of the machine, two pieces of wood (2″ x 1″ x 4′) can be inserted down the left-hand side of the machine between the tub and cabinet to support the tub during its removal. **Note:** If your machine has the timer on the opposite side to that shown in the diagram, the wood should be inserted down the right-hand side and the machine laid over correspondingly.

Now lower the machine onto the left-hand side after making sure that the cabinet side and floor are protected, and release the shock absorber or friction damper mountings. Now disconnect the sump hose, pressure hoses, heater connections, thermostat connections and motor block connections. Remove drive belt and drum pulley and check that all connections are free from the outer tub unit. At the top of the machine, release the suspension springs by pushing the tub unit towards the top of the machine. It will now be possible to slide the tub assembly out of the cabinet. At this point a little help may be useful as the unit will be quite heavy and needs manoeuvring out of position. At this time ensure that the lower friction plate is being supported by one of the wooden strips. Hold the door open during the tub withdrawal.

Once removed, the unit is then easily accessible and the bearing renewal is similar to that shown in the previous photo sequence. Make a note of all clamp positions, tub front and back positions, etc. It is advisable to re-seal and check all hoses and their fixing points prior to refitting the unit. It is important to do this when the tub is out of the machine as this may be difficult when the unit is replaced.

Refitting is a reversal of the removal procedure. After refitting, ensure that all electrical and earth connections are replaced correctly and securely and an R.C.D. protected socket

is used when the functional test sequence is carried out.
Note: Many manufacturers now have machines on the market with detachable front panels, Philips, Fagor and Hotpoint are three of these. The latter being the version with the plastic/nylon outer tub, see Hotpoint photo sequence. With this type of machine, the drum and bearing assemblies can be removed and changed with the outer tub *in situ*, thus avoiding the extra work involved in tub removal. Plastic/nylon outer tubs are now used on some combined washerdrier machines.

With the Hotpoint machine, the pulley is threaded to the shaft and is secured by a locknut. To release the pulley, chock it with wood and rotate the drum anti-clockwise from the front of the machine. When refitting, apply some locking compound to the shaft thread (this can be obtained from any good D.I.Y. or motorists shop).

This picture shows a Fagor machine with the front panel removed, illustrating the excellent access that can be found with this type of machine.

Diagram 1.

Diagram 2.

Chapter 31

Using a meter

Throughout this book, references have been made to meters and their use in continuity testing of individual parts of appliances and their connecting wires. All such testing and checking for 'open' (i.e. not allowing for current flow), or 'closed' circuit (i.e. allowing current to flow), must be carried out using a battery powered multi-meter or test meter. **Under no circumstances should testing be carried out on 'live' items**, i.e. appliances connected to the mains supply.
Remember: completely isolate the appliances from the mains supply before starting any repair work or testing.

Although some meters and testers have the facility to check mains voltages, I do not agree with their use in repairs to domestic appliances. Faults can be easily traced by simple low voltage (battery power) continuity testing, proving that the simplest of meters or even a homemade one like the one described are perfectly adequate for some faults. Remember that safety is paramount and under no circumstances should it be compromised. Always double check that the appliance is unplugged; a good tip is to keep the plug in view so that no- one else can inadvertently plug it in. The simple home-made continuity tester described later will help trace faults in the

wiring of the appliance only. A multimeter like the ones shown will be required for any component testing.

If you decide to buy a test meter, you could find yourself faced with quite a variety to choose from. Do not be tempted to an get over complicated one as it could end up confusing and misleading you when in use. Before using your new meter, read the manufacturer's instructions

A typical test meter of the type to be bought in most DIY stores. Try to obtain a meter with a good informative booklet. The meter shown was purchased for under £14.00 and proved to be useful for many other jobs around the house and car.

This simple continuity tester was purchased from a local automart for only £2. It is a manufactured version of the home made type described.

The test on this outlet pump stator coil proved to be O.K. (i.e. closed circuit/continuity). This meant that the supply or neutral to and from the pump required checking to discover the reason why the pump failed to work at any point in the programme.

A simple test is all that is required to trace harness faults.

The testing of the heater element to check for a circuit 'through it'. In this instance, the heater does have a circuit as shown by the meter needle. This means that the 'no heat' fault on the machine is not a fault of this component. The next step would be to test the wiring and connections to and from the heater in the same way. Also check the timer and/or the thermostat if in the heater circuit.

A multimeter of the type to be found in most DIY stores. Try to obtain a meter with a good information booklet. The meter shown was purchased for under £10.00 and proved to be useful for many other jobs around the house and car.

The testing of this water valve proved that the coil was open circuit. This is shown by the meter needle staying at its 'rest' position. This shows that the 'no fill' fault on the machine was in fact due to the water valve failing to energize and allow water into the machine. (On components such as these, it is a good idea to try to move the terminals as a poor internal connection may cause the bad reading). This problem, was cured by renewing the valve.

thoroughly and make sure that you fully understand them. The meter used in the photographs is simple to use when continuity testing and has a scale that reads 'open' circuit or 'closed' circuit. It was purchased from a local DIY store and was very reasonably priced. The meter will also help locate faults with car electrics, but as previously stated, using on live mains circuits should not be entertained.

Some multi-meters are able to show the resistance value of the item being tested as well as indicating continuity. This can be extremely useful if the correct value of the item being tested is known, i.e. correct resistance of motor winding, armature and element, etc., although this is by no means essential. Detailed use of the multi-meter for this function will be found in its accompanying instruction leaflet.

ELECTRICAL FAULT FINDING

A simple continuity tester for wiring. This simple device can be used to trace wiring faults in most appliances and is very easy to make. It uses the lack of continuity to its full advantage. To make this tester, you will need a standard battery, bulb and three wires (1 x 5″ and 2 x 10″). Connect the short wire to the positive terminal of the battery and the other end of that wire to the centre terminal of a small torch bulb. Attach one of the longer wires to the negative terminal of the battery and leave the other end free. The other wire should be attached to the body of the bulb again, leave the end free.

The two loose ends now act as the test wires. Press the two ends of the wires together, and the bulb will light. If not, check that the battery and the bulb and all connections are OK. When 'open circuit', the light will stay off, and when 'closed

circuit', the light will be on.
*Note: Low voltage bulb type testers of 1.5 volts or 3 volts are unsuitable for testing the continuity of components within the machines. A test meter like the ones shown will be required to test high resistance items such as pumps, timer coil, valves etc. Ensure that the machine is isolated from the main supply before attempting to use a meter.

HOW TO TEST FOR CONTINUITY USING A TEST METER

To test for an open circuit, note and remove the original wiring to the component to be tested. (If this is not done, false readings may be given from other items that may be in circuit.) The ends of the two wires of the meter should be attached to the component that is suspected. For example, to test a heater for continuity, place the metal probes on the tags at the end of the heater and watch the meter. The needle should move.

If the heater is 'open circuit', i.e. No movement, the heater can then be suspected and tested further. If closed circuit, the heater continuity is OK.

Often the most effective way to trace a fault is to use a very simple, but logical approach to them. One such approach is called the leap frog method and can be used to find the failed/open circuit part or parts. In this instance, let us assume that the appliance does not work at all when functionally tested, therefore you cannot deduce where the problem lies purely from the symptoms. A quick check of the supply socket by plugging in another appliance known to be OK will verify (or not) that there is power up to that point. This confirms that the fault lies somewhere in the appliance, its supply cable or plug. We know that during normal conditions, power flows in through the live pin on the plug, through the appliance (when switches on) and returns via the neutral pin on the plug. The fact that the appliance will not work at all even when plugged in and switched on indicates that an open circuit exists somewhere along this normal live to neutral circuit.

LEAP FROG TESTING – USING A METER

First, test that the meter is working correctly, i.e. touch test probes together and the meter should indicate continuity. With the machine unplugged (isolated) connect one probe to the live pin of the appliance's plug and the other on the live conductor connecting point in the plug. Continuity should be found which confirms that the pin, fuse and their connections are alright, but faulty if open circuit occurs. If this check proves to be OK, move the probe from the live conductor point in the plug to the live conductor connection in the terminal block within the appliance. Again, continuity should be found, if not, a fault between plug and terminal block is indicated. **Note:** On cable continuity testing, it is best to move the cable along its length during the test to ascertain if an intermittent fault may exist. If this test is alright, proceed to move the probe to the next convenient point along the live conductor, in this instance, the supply side of the on/off switch, which may be part of the main programme switch on some machines (usually the front terminals).

Again, continuity is required. An open circuit indicates a fault between terminal block and switch connection. The next step is to move the probe to the opposite terminal of the switch. Operate the switch to verify correct action (i.e. 'on' continuity, 'off' open circuit). If OK proceed to the next point along the wire, in this instance the interlock connection. Again continuity is required. If OK, move probe to the terminal on the return side of the heater within the interlock (See: Door switches (interlocks) chapter). This again should indicate continuity through heater of the interlock. At this point we will assume that an open circuit has been indicated, so go back to the last test point and verify continuity up to that point. If found to be alright, than a fault has been traced that lies within the interlock which requires renewal.

This simple, methodical approach is all that is required to find such problems. With more complex circuits it is best to break them down into individual sections, i.e. motor, heater, switch, etc., and test continuity of each section from live through the timer and the individual parts and back to neutral. This may involve moving the live probe that would normally remain on the plug live pin to a more convenient supply point within the appliance to avoid misleading continuity readings from other items within the appliance circuit. With practice, faults can be found even in complex wiring in this way.
Note: The action of switching within the interlock of power

back to the timer cannot be verified but continuity of the wiring can be checked in a similar leap frog manner. In this instance, due to the heater being 'open circuit' the interlock would fail to operate and the action of power being returned (switched) to the timer for distribution to other parts could not take place. A fault with the main switching action of the interlock would have been indicated during the functional test (See: Functional testing), i.e. when the machine was switched on, the door locked but nothing else would operate other than the door locking. This is due to most (but not all) machines having the interlock as the first item in circuit when switched on, therefore incorrect latching of the door or failure of the interlock (other than short circuit of the internal switch) will render the appliance inoperable.

DO NOT trace faults by looking for mains voltages. There is no need to consider or use such dangerous techniques. All testing can and should be carried out with the appliance completely isolated (i.e. switch off, plug out), using only a battery powered meter or tester to indicate continuity or open circuit.

The ohms reading will differ from item to item. Test for open or closed circuits only. Any reference to an ohm (Ω) reading is a guide only as resistances differ from machine to machine. The objective is to test for either continuity or the lack of continuity of the item being tested.

Chapter 32

Wiring and harness faults

WHAT IS A WIRING HARNESS?

The term harness is used for all of the wires that connect the various components within the appliance. On large appliances they are usually bound or fastened together in bunches to keep the wiring in the appliance neat and safely anchored. Smaller appliances, however, may sacrifice neatness for safety and route the wiring to avoid contact with heat, sharp edges, etc.

WHAT DOES IT DO?

At first sight, the harness may look like a jumble of wires thrown together. This is not the case. If you take the time to inspect the harness, you will find that each wire is colour coded or numbered (either on the wire itself, or on the connector at either end). This allows you to follow the wiring through the appliance easily. With practice, any wiring or coding can be followed.

As most of the wires in the machine either finish or start at the timer unit, it may be helpful to think of the timer as the base of a tree, with the main wiring harness as the trunk. As

Harness connector block. Again any loose connectors will overheat and cause problems. Ensure a secure fit.

the trunk is followed, branches appear (wires to the valves, pressure switches, etc.). Continuing upwards, the trunk gets slowly thinner as branching takes place to the motor, pump, module, etc.

Each item is therefore separate but linked to the timer by a central bond of wire. This in turn can be likened to a central command post, communicating with field outposts.

The connecting wires to and/or from a component are vital to that component and possibly others that rely on the correct functioning of that item.

Luckily, wiring faults are not too common, but when they do occur they sometimes appear to result in big problems, when in reality it is only a small fault that has occurred, i.e. one poor connection can cause a motor not to function at all, and render the appliance unusable.

Do not fall into the trap of always suspecting the worst. Many people, including engineers, blindly fit parts such as a motor or a heater for a similar fault to that mentioned, only to find it did not cure the problem. Often the timer is blamed and subsequently changed. This does not cure the problem and is an expensive

The terminal block is the first distribution point of the power into the machine. Ensure all connections are sound, as heat will be generated if not.

Ribbon cable is often used in computer-controlled machines.

Male Terminal   Female Terminal

Harness connection. Can often be of a multi block fitting of several wires in one moulded block.

Insulation cover.

Female spade terminal.

In line connector used for low amperage.

Butt connector for connecting several wires together.

Piggy back terminal for two wires to one terminal.

All of the above are 'crimp' fitted to inner and outer of the wires. When used make sure that they fit securely and will not easily part.

Large in line connector used for high amperage wires.

mistake. Stop, think and check all wires and connections that relate to your particular fault. Always inspect all connections and ensure that the wire and connector has a tight fit. Loose or poor connections can overheat and cause a lot of trouble, especially on items such as the heater.

Poor connections to items such as the main motor or pump will be aggravated by movement of the machine when in use and may not be so apparent when a static test is carried out.

One of the most easily missed faults is where the metal core (conductor) of the wire has broken and the outer insulation has not. This wire will appear perfect from the outside but will pass no electrical current. To test for this, see the chapter: Using a meter.

It must be remembered that such faults may be intermittent. That is to say that one reading

All of the above are 'crimp' fitted to inner and outer of the wires. When used make sure that they fit securely and will not easily part.

may be correct and the same test later may prove incorrect. This is due to the movement of the outer insulation of the wire first making, then breaking the electrical connection.

When testing for such intermittent faults, pull or stretch each wire tested. An unbroken wire will not stretch whereas a wire that is broken internally will stretch at the break point and rectification is a simple matter of renewing the connection with a suitable connector. Do not make the connection by twisting the wires together and covering them with insulation tape. Use only the correct rating of connector and ensure a secure and insulated joint. If a joint is required in a position of cable

movement, e.g. wiring from shell to tub unit components, it is advisable to renew the whole length of wiring or the joint made in a fixed section of cable. The use of rigid connections in movable wiring must be avoided. Take time to do a few simple checks. It saves time, patience and money.

Note: Ensure that the harness is secured adequately to the shell of the machine, at the same time allowing for free movement of the motor, heater etc.

Take care that any metal fastening clips do not chafe the plastic insulation around the wires. Also make sure that wires are not in contact with sharp metal edges such as self tapping screws etc.

Warning: Before attempting to remove or repair the wiring harness or any other component in the appliance, isolate the appliance from the main electrical supply by removing the plug from the wall socket.

Chapter 33

Dry-only machines

models with a 6 lb (2.7 kg) load capacity, convenient if space is restricted, operates in exactly the same way as the larger models.

B. The larger drum allows for better movement of the clothing through the airflow, ensuring more even and quicker drying even as the clothing increases in bulk during the drying process. Remember, this increase in the bulk of the load is why the combined washerdrier machines can dry only half its wash load.

The tumbledrier has been with us for many years now. The basic function is to circulate warm air through the damp clothes for a given period of time selected by the user, which is then followed by a cool tumble prior to switching off at the end of the selected time. This is a relatively simple opeation requiring a drum to hold the load, a heater to warm the air and a fan to circulate the warm air through the drum. As with combined washerdrier machines, the drum is rotated to allow all the load to gain maximum benefit from the warm air flow. In most tumble dry only machines the motor that revolves the drum also drives the fan used for air circulation. Being a dedicated machine (drying only) it works much more efficiently than its combined washerdrier counterpart. There are several reasons for this:

A. The drum capacity can be much larger. As it is not necessary to have a water tight outer tub thusd allowing for a larger drum taking up nearly all the available space within the cabinet. The larger machines (those with cabinets the same size as a washing machine) can take the same size load, i.e. an 11 lb (5 kg) wash load can be transferred directly into the 11 lb load tumbledrier. The smaller

This diagram depicts a condenser style tumble dry only machine which utilises a cold air flow duct to remove the moisture from the sealed warm air flow. Action is as follows: Air within the sealed system is circulated by fan (E) over heater unit (D) and on into the drum (B). Moisture is picked up by the warm air flow (C) and after passing through a fluff filter, is directed over a cool metal ducting or plate (G). The moisture condenses on the much cooler surface and collects in a sump beneath. The condensing plate or duct is kept cool by constant circulation of air created by fan (H). Air is drawn in at (J) and vented at (I). For ease of emptying, the condensate water is transferred by pump (F) to the reservoir tank (A) which requires regular emptying. Alternatively, the machine can be plumbed to a suitable drain/outlet, therefore eliminating the need for manual emptying of the reservoir.

C. A larger wattage heater can be used (if necessary) with a greater surface area for warming the air due to more space available for such components. D. Again, due to the increase in usable space a larger fan can be used for circulating the air.

Over the years, additions to the basic principles have been made. Drum rotation on early and current basic machines is in one direction only. Nowadays, the option is to have reverse drum action similar to the wash action (clockwise and counter clockwise). This obviously requires a more complex motor which is capable of rotation in both directions, and a more complex timer or motor reversal system. Temperature control, again on early and current basic models is relatively straightforward with selections of high or low, but on the more recent and expensive machines, auto sensing is now a feature. This system senses the moisture content of the load being dried and switches off when a pre-selected degree of dryness has been reached. The advantage of auto-sensing is that it switches off when dry unlike the more basic machine that carries on tumbling and heating for the set time regardless of whether the clothes are dry or not.

Further refinements and extras include computer control (electronic in place of mechanical), intermittent tumble after the drying process is complete which prevents the load compacting at the end of the cycle if left unattended for any length of time prior to removal. Condenser tumbledriers are also available. These operate in a similar manner to the combined washerdrier system by condensing the moisture rather than venting it. Some require water supply and outlet whilst others use cold air instead of water to aid condensing, and a removable container to collect the

condensate. The container requires regular emptying (once every two dry cycles on average if not permanently drained in a similar way to the automatic washer, i.e. pump and outlet).

The tumbledriers covered in this book heat the air used in the drying process by electricity, but domestic tumbledriers are now available which heat by gas. Although commercial machines have had this option for several years, it is new to the domestic user. Because of the stringent gas regulations and the obvious need for safety, do not attempt installation or any inspection or repair on this type of product. The installation and repair of gas appliances must be done by those with the relevant knowledge, equipment and gas qualifications.

The main benefits of the larger dry-only machines (same sized cabinet as the washing machine), are that it will dry a full wash load, and it can also be drying one load whilst another load is being washed, thus saving a lot of time. **Note:** Do not use both machines from a single socket via an adaptor. See: Basics – Electrical. The separate drier is also quicker and more efficient than combined washerdriers if used correctly.

As already described, tumbledriers operate by tumbling the damp clothes in a warm flow of air within the drum. There are two different ways in which this airflow through the clothes can be created – by suction and by pressurisation. Both systems however have the same basic components of drive motor, heater, thermostat, tension pulley and timer. The difference lies in the way the airflow is created.

THE SUCTION SYSTEM

With this system the airflow is created by a large extractor fan,

usually belt driven (elastic type) by the same motor which is used to rotate the drum by means of a second belt (narrow multi 'V' type). When the drying programme has been selected and switched on, the fan and the drum both rotate. The rotating fan draws air from within the drum and expels it through a vent at the rear of the machine. The cabinet of the machine forms a partially sealed system with an air inlet grille positioned some distance from the fan vent. Air is drawn in through this inlet grille to replace the air extracted from the drum by the fan. The semi-sealed system directs the cold air which is drawn in, to pass over the heating elements (the position of which may vary depending on make of machine), on its way to the drum, through the clothes, picking up moisture as it does so, and out via the extractor fan vent, thus drying the load in the process. At the onset of the cool tumble (10–15 minutes before the end of the selected drying time), the heater is turned off but drum rotation and fan action continues creating a cool air flow for the remainder of the cycle.

Felt seals are used to ensure that air is only drawn in from the drum and not from the shell space as this would result in poor drying and reduced air flow over the heating element. A removable filter is positioned within the air flow path to trap any fluff or lint and prevent it being blown from the vent.

THE PRESSURISED SYSTEM

The efficiency of this system relies on the shell of the machine being sealed to prevent air entering or escaping through any other than the correct positions. It is essential that the panels are fitted correctly and that all sealing felt or foam strips fitted on removable parts such as back panel, lid or facia

MOISTURE LADEN AIR

MOISTURE LADEN AIR

HOT AIR

COLD AIR

A typical suction system of a tumble dry only machine.
A. Spiral heating element.
B. Door.
C. Main motor for drum and fan drive.
D. Fan pulley and elasticated belt.
E. Drum.
F. Fluff filter and felt seals.
G. Suction/vent fan.
H. Tension pulley and belt.

parts are in good order or renewed if damaged. Air flow is created by drawing air in via the inlet grille by a centrifugal fan mounted directly on the main motor shaft. This creates a slight pressure build-up within the sealed shell of the appliance.

The drum inner has an exhaust vent usually to the rear of the machine although some models vent to the front via the door, or via a duct to a grille at the lower of the front panel. For the pressurised air to escape through the vent, it must first pass through the heating elements where it is heated, on through the drum and clothing,

and through a removable fluff/lint trap before escaping through the exhaust vent.

In machines using either of these systems, thermostats are used to monitor the exhaust air temperature which can open circuit the heating element(s) at predetermined temperature(s). This action ensures that an optimum drying temperature is maintained without excessive use of power, i.e. heating an already dry load. Normally, as the warm air passes through the damp clothing during the drying process, its temperature drops as it picks up moisture from the clothing. On basic machines the time selected for drying is judged by the user, but if the selected time is too long for a particular load, the warm air passing through it when dry will not cool and actuate the exhaust thermostat and open circuit the heater. The thermostats used are of the self-setting type, therefore cycling of this action will occur until the remainder of the timed heat cycle has ended and the cool tumble begins. Usually, a double

A typical pressurised system of a tumble dry only machine.
A. Solid heating element/s.
B. Drum.
C. Fluff filter.
D. Felt seal.
E. Air inlet grille.
F. Fan (centrifugal type).
G. Main motor.
H. Tension pulley and belt.

temperature thermostat is used in conjunction with high and low heat settings and is designed to maintain a predetermined air tempeature throughout the drying cycle whilst at the same time providing an overheat safeguard. Thermostat temperature ratings differ from one make to another and also between models from the same manufacturer, as the temperature ratings are matched to the performances and heater wattage of each machine. Make sure that when required, only the correct replacement thermostat is obtained for your machine. For operation and testing of thermostats, see Temperature control chapter.

Note: On computer-controlled or auto-sensing machines, a combination of fixed thermostats and thermistors or resistance probes will be encountered. The configuration depends on the make and model of the machine.

TUMBLEDRIER FUNCTIONAL TEST

Purpose of the test: To test where practical the main functions of the tumbledrier and its installation in the more efficient manner.

1. Ensure that the door of the machine is closed – turn the programme timer to 20 minutes.
2. Check that the drum rotates. If the drier is of the reversing type (drum rotation of clockwise and counter clockwise) check for this action. Length of rotation and pause times differ greatly between makes, so be patient and familiarise yourself with the correct action of your machine.
3. Open the door and confirm that the drum stops. Confirm that warm air is present in the drum. **Note:** On some machines, closing the door restarts the cycle whereas other machines need to be restarted by pushing the reset button after the door has been closed.
4. Select the other heat settings (if applicable) and repeat steps 2 and 3 to confirm that heating is taking place.
5. Allow the timer to advance to the anti-crease cycle (cool down to 10 to 15 minutes prior to end of programme), and confirm that cold air is now circulating in the drum.
Let this action run for 5–10 minutes.
6. Monitor the machine noise during all operations. If excessive, terminate test, isolate the machine prior to inspection.

If the drier is permanently vented or a vent hose is normally used, check that it is clear. Check the outlet of the hose or vent during steps 2 and 5, making sure that there is a good flow of air present.
Note: Some machines may incorporate a second user selectable timer of up to 12 hours time delay. This timer is used to interrupt the main timing control, allowing the timer to be used more economically on reduced rate electrical supply (e.g. Economy 7). To test this timer, select the shortest time delay possible and ensure that the main timer is also set. Normal action of the machine should commence only after the delay timer has reached the end of the delay selected.

REGULAR INSPECTION POINTS – TUMBLE DRY ONLY MACHINES

De-linting, a vital cleaning procedure relating to the safety and efficiency of tumble dry-only machines.

Regular inspection of tumbledriers is vital, not only to keep them in good working order but also to ensure that accumulations of lint and fluff do not build up within the machine constituting a possible danger of fire. It is recommended that the following procedure be carried out on a regular basis, the time period of which is dependent on the degree of usage but should be no longer than twelve months between inspections. The same procedure should also be carried out if a repair is required between the normal routine inspections. A thorough stripdown of the appliance is required to ensure that all components are free from lint/fluff and that all wiring connections are secure and in good condition. Do not relegate this procedure to a quick inspection and a cleaning of only those parts that are easily accessible with only the top of the machine removed.

Due to the many variations of machines available, a description of how each should be stripped down cannot be given in detail. However, a basic sequence which will suit most if not all machines is as follows and as always should only be carried out with the machine fully isolated.

1. Check and clean the removable filter. This, of course should not be unduly blocked as cleaning of this item should be part of the normal usage routine.
2. Remove the vent hose (if fitted) and check the outlet duct of the machine for fluff build up. The full length of the hose or ducting should also be checked along with external grilles on permanently vented systems. Ensure the whole system is free from restrictions.
3. Always, take notes of components, wiring connections and routing within the machine prior to stripdown or removal.
4. Ensure each component is thoroughly cleaned and all traces of lint/fluff removed. This should be done with care using a small dusting brush and/or cylinder vacuum cleaner.
5. Particular attention should be paid to components such as the timer(s), main motor (cooling grilles, etc.), T.O.C.s, thermostats, terminal connections, heating elements and fixing points. Solid elements (sheathed) can be brushed clean but spiral elements must be carefully cleaned to avoid stretching or damage to their ceramic holders. With spiral elements, fluff may build up within the hollow centre. This can best be removed by carefully teasing it free with a needle or similar item.
6. Renew any suspect or worn components, overheated/poor connections, worn drive belt(s), tension pulley(s). Ensure correct position and lubricate if required, drum support bearings for wear and heater support brackets/cord.
7. Re-assemble the machine ensuring that all wiring,

protective covers, supports and seals are correctly positioned and fitted.

8. Test for earth continuity as detailed in the Basics – Electrical and Using a Meter chapters.

9. Refer to Basic-Electrical chapter and check condition of both plug and socket, i.e. for overheating, damage and correct supply.

10. Functionally test the machine on an R.C.D. protected supply.

Tumble dry only machines are, in essence simple machines. but it is advisable to make oneself aware of capabilities and limitations of these machines. When cleaning the filter you may be surprised by the quantity of fluff and lint that it has accumulated. However, if used correctly, tumbledriers do not unduly stress the fabrics they dry. It takes around 1000 tumble dry cycles for an 8 oz (227 grammes) item of clothing to lose 1 oz (28 grammes) in this way.

Remember also that the length of time your drier takes is proportional to the efficiency and spin speed of your washing machine. It is a fact that all fabric contains a degree of moisture when they are dry. Unfortunately it is possible to over-dry clothing in a tumbledrier (or combined machine) and so remove the natural balanced moisture content of the fabric which leads to shrinkage, excessive static and wrinkling that will not iron out. Such problems often lead to the machine being blamed when it is often the user that is at fault by selecting a dry setting that is too long, too high a heat setting or both.

Take into consideration the load content and size when setting the timer, if in doubt, refer to the machine's instruction booklet. This will not only help avoid over-drying problems, but will also save money by reducing the amount of electricity consumed.

Whenever possible, avoid drying woollen items in a tumbledrier as they are particularly prone to the afore mentioned problems.

Articles made from or containing foam, sponge, plastic, wax coatings or printed surfaces should not be dried in a tumbledrier as they too can easily be heat damaged and could possibly constitute a fire hazard.

Above all DO NOT use any tumbledrier to dry clothing or materials that have been previously cleaned with flammable spirits or dry fluids. Ensure any such articles are left in a well ventilated area to be fully aired and DO NOT subject them to a dry cycle until they have been washed.

Keep filters clean and renew if damaged, i.e. torn or distorted.

Popular small front venting tumble dry only machine.

Large rear fan housing of a 9lb load early Hoover machine. The fan is driven by an elasticated belt directly from the motor shaft which also drives the main drum. The motor in this instance is a large shaded pole motor with multi 'V' belt drive at one end and round pulley at the other.

Ensure thermostats are fitted correctly and free from fluff build-ups that act as insulation leading to incorrect temperature sensing.

Inspect heating element closely for fluff contamination, sagging or breakages like the one shown. Complete heater units are generally not expensive.

Through lack of regular maintenance, fluff has built up on and around the heating elements. It can be seen from the photo that the build-up is charred and has smouldered. This is a potential fire risk. Regular de-linting is essential to avoid this problem.

It is common for the front lip on the drum to be used as the front support bearing. Ensure that it is smooth and undamaged. It will either be supported by a simple felt strip coated in PTFE or by plastic mounts which act as support bearings. All variations are prone to wear.

When de-linting, check all areas of the machine. In this instance the motor is in need of a thorough cleaning, not only in order to function correctly, but also for safety.

Elasticated belts are prone to stretching and fraying. Renew them regularly to maintain peak performance from your machine.

Many Creda machine use a braided webbing as a front bearing. It is glued to the front drum lip and rests on the metal edge of the shell of the machine. When worn, the machine will vibrate badly and become very noisy. Renewing the webbing is straightforward, but it is wise to remove all traces of paint from the worn shell lip and make sure that it is smooth. Lubricate both parts with PTFE prior to reassembly.

This 6 lb load machine has a wrap around outer shell with no obvious means of access.

First remove the two screws found on the lower edge of each side of the machine.

Worn tension pulleys can create a lot of noise or allow the belt to constantly slip or jump out of position. Renew if worn or damaged; also check the supporting shaft for wear. Whenever possible renew both parts as a set as shown.

PTFE lubricant as required by webbing type bearing.

Lowering the door exposed a further four screws.

A note of all screws was made as different sizes were encountered.

With all eight screws removed, the one piece outer shell of the machine would slide out of position vertically.

Removing the outer shell exposed the induction motor, drum belt, tension pulley system and door microswitch with actuating arm.

Although not as bad as expected, de-linting of the motor, motor relay, microswitch and tension pulley system was required. The drum belt was inspected and found to be OK.

Checking of the front bearing required the removal of the bolts from the front of the side stays and the removal of the wiring to the timer (a note of all connections were made prior to removal).

With the wiring and fixings removed, the front of the machine could be eased forward to expose the front bearing and drum lip.

Close inspection of the plastic support pads, drum lip and sealing felt was made. In this instance they were sound and only required cleaning.

FAULT FINDING GUIDE

Most of the fault symptoms listed below will relate to mechanically timed and computer-controlled machines both of which are mechanically similar and differ only in the way they are controlled, see Timers chapter.

Symptom 1. Won't work at all

Possible cause	Action
a. Faulty mains lead, plug or socket	See Plugs and Sockets chapter. Check mains lead for continuity see – Using a meter
b. Door not closed or latched correctly	Re-close door and ensure it is latched correctly
c. Door micro-switch failed (O/C)	Check switch action (audible clicks when door is open/closed) and verify continuity, see – Using a meter. Inspect closely for overheating and renew if suspect.
d. Timer fault	Check switching action of manual timers (audible clicks) and continuity. Check for loose selector knob on shaft of timer, i.e. rotating but not setting timer cams or mechanism. On computer-controlled machines, check all wiring edge connections to and from the circuit board.

The removal of the back panel (held only in position by self tapping screws) allowed access to the fan, heater unit and T.O.C.

Although clean and free from lint, the element had a broken ceramic insulator. The T.O.C. also showed signs of contact damage and both parts were duly renewed prior to re-assembly.

Re-assembly was a simple reversal of the strip down procedure. Ensure that all seals are sound and that all fixing screws are refitted in their original positions. The removable shell locates in slides on both sides and top of the front panel.

Symptom 2. Machine works but no heat.

Possible Cause	Action
a. Insufficient time set	Remember that the last 15 mins approx. of cycle is a cool tumble on most machines. If a time of less than 15 mins is selected the heater will not be energised, only drum action.
b. Open circuit auto reset T.O.C. on heater	Check heater T.O.C. for continuity, see Using a meter.
c. Tripped manual reset T.O.C.	Check thoroughly for blockages or restrictions to air intakes, filter and exhaust vents/hoses before resetting T.O.C.
d. Broken/O.C. element	Check condition of heating element(s) and for continuity. Renew if suspect.
e. Open circuit (O.C.) exhaust thermostat (if fitted) or thermistors on computer machines	Check for continuity of stat and of wiring.
f. Faulty timer	On manual timers check action of heater switch and continuity. With computer-controlled machines check all connections to and from the P.C.B. If OK, possible fault of control board or relay used to switch elements. Eliminate all other possible causes before changing this item.

Symptom 3. Heats and trips T.O.C. but no drum action.

Possible cause	Action
a. Broken drive belt	Check belt and renew as required.
b. Door micro-switch O/C (some models only)	Some machines link the door micro-switch into the motor circuit only. Check door is latched correctly and the switch for continuity and any damage. Renew if suspect.
Belt slipping	Check for overload of clothing and condition of belt, see Belts chapter. Check drive pulley of motor, position and tension of jockey pulley(s).

d. Open circuit motor

Check for free rotation of drum motor. Also, is motor choked with fluff? Clean if required. Check for continuity of T.O.C. and windings. If capacitor start, see Motors chapter. If centrifugal start, check action/free movement of this system within the motor. Some early motors had manual reset T.O.C.s. Check motor thoroughly before resetting.

e. Faulty timer

On manual timers, check action of motor switch and continuity. With computer-controlled machines, check all connections to and from the P.C.B. If OK, possible fault on control board. Eliminate all other possible causes before changing this item.

Symptom 4. Works for a while and stops and restarts after 10/15 mins (if manual timer has not timed out).

Possible cause	Action
a. Motor overheating and tripping it's self-setting TOC	Common fault on several machines for various reasons. Check for the following: fluff blockage in and around the motor or air intake grilles. Worn bearings on motor end frames allowing rotor to chafe on stator as motor runs. Loose cooling fan on motor. Motor overheating due to internal wiring fault. Temperamental TOC within motor windings tripping at normal working temperature, often caused by infrequent cleaning of motor. Worn drum bearings slowing both drum and motor causing overheat within the motor. The majority of these problems can be avoided by regular cleaning.

Symptom 5. Noisy when in use

Possible cause	Action
a. Drum bearings worn	Check condition of both front and rear bearings.
b(i) Loose fan (pressurised machines)	Check that large centrifugal fan on main motor is secure on shaft and is not rotating independent of it. Ensure that

	the fan is not damaged or catching on other items. Renew if suspect.
b(ii) Fan shaft/bearings worn (suction machines)	Check for excessive movement of both pulley and shaft. The shaft should be free to rotate without lateral movement. Renew if found to be worn.

Note: b(i) and b(ii) also relate to poor drying of load. (a) can relate to black or other marks being left on clothing dried in the machine.

c. Worn or damaged jockey pulley(s)	This type of fault can give rise to a chattering noise if the pulley is damaged or a high pitched squeaking noise if dry. Check for excessive wear on pulley shaft, i.e. lateral movement. Renew if damaged or suspect in any way. If OK, lubricate pulley centre support shaft.
d. Loose, worn or broken motor mount	Inspect motor mounting closely and renew if suspect.
e. Loose panels or facia parts	Ensure all covers and panels, etc., are fitted correctly and that all seals (if fitted) are in good order. Make sure all securing screws are fitted and are tight.

Symptom 6. Machine works but poor drying performance.

Possible cause	Action
a. Too little drying time selected for load	Reset timer for sufficient time to dry the load. See instruction booklet for guide to drying times for your machine.
b. Incorrect heat setting selected	Check that the low heat setting was not set for fabrics needing extra heat, eg. cottons. See instruction booklet for more information.
c. Heater self-setting TOC tripping	Check for restrictions in filter and all air vents. If OK, check TOC continuity. If nuisance tripping is suspected (tired TOC), renew with correct replacement.
d. Open circuit (O.C.) heater	Check condition and continuity of heater.

e. Vent thermostat fault

Check for continuity.

f. Recycling of exhaust air

If the machine is not vented correctly, it is possible that the moist air expelled from the exhaust vent could be taken back into the machine via the air intake vent.
Check for this action and rectify if found.

Symptom 7. Excessively tangled clothing*

Possible cause

Action

a. Loose or worn drum drive belt

Check condition of drive belt, see Belt chapter. Ensure correct position of jockey pulley(s) and that the tension spring is OK.

b. Rotation of drum too slow

Check for overloading and drum bearings for wear or binding which may slow drum rotation.

*Tangling of the load is more likely to occur in omni-directional rotating dryers than in reversing models.

Computer-controlled (electronically controlled) machines are often capable of a degree of self-diagnosis. When a fault or problem occurs, a fault code will be displayed on the L.E.D. or L.C.D. display panel. Occasionally the display will describe the fault, but more common is the display of a range of alpha numerical codes, eg. F1, E4, etc. The code indicated relates to a particular problem detected by the micro-processor. Reference to the manufacturer's instruction booklet will give the meaning of each code. See Timers chapter for more detail. The machine will not continue with the remainder of the programme setting until the fault has been rectified. Although the fault display codings may differ from one manufacturer to another, many of the faults they indicate are covered on the list of symptoms 1–7.

Faults which are uncommon or difficult to isolate may be caused by poor connections to, or faults within the electronic control boards, or penetration by moisture due to faulty or incorrectly positioned seals. Ensure that all connections, covers and seals are sound and correctly fitted and eliminate all other possible faults before changing a control panel. As stated in the Timers chapter all circuit testing on micro-processor-controlled machines must be carried out using a low voltage tester, i.e. 1.5 volts to avoid damage to the electronic components. Do not handle the components of the circuit boards as damage can also be done by static discharged from the fingers.

This type of damage is not always immediately apparent. However, static discharges can corrupt the processor chip's internal programme memory and result in unusual and often intermittent fault symptoms, some time after the initial damage was done. Handle the boards only by the edges if it is absolutely necessary.

Another feature of electronically-controlled machines is that a self-diagnostic functional test routing can be initiated. How the sequence is started differs with makes and models and is usually restricted to service personnel. Most machines need to be turned off (at the socket) for at least 45 seconds to clear any previously set programme. Starting the functional test then requires the pressing of two of the selector buttons simultaneously whilst switching the machine on. this sequence is used only to highlight the way in which a test sequence may be initiated and does not indicate the way in which any particular machine would operate. owing to the number of different ways in which this system can be set, it is impossible to give specific details in this text.

Chapter 34

Useful tips and information

An R.C.D. is essential.

For damage or rust to the shell of your machine, domestic appliance white paint is available. Shown are spray and brush on types.

Combined washerdrier machines often require sealant at joints or connection points. Always renew damage or disturbed sealant. Due to the high temperatures and damp conditions, it is essential that only the correct sealant is used.

Tumble drier bearing faults often require PTFE lubrication. This is available in liquid or spray form.

When removing the wire door seal securing band on some machines it is advisable to wear eye protection. This is also essential when drifting out old bearings. Wear sturdy gloves to protect your hands from the rough casting or other sharp edges when handling cast aluminium pulleys.

Check all hoses thoroughly for perishing and/or cracking. With corrugated hoses (as shown), stretch the hose to ensure a thorough check. (It is wise to check any new hose before fitting).

Sealants like the one shown can be used for pressure system hoses and for aiding the fitting and sealing of new hoses, grommets, etc.

A little washing-up liquid or fabric conditioner can be smeared on grommets or rubber mouldings.

Some machines may have a wire surrounding the door seal. This retaining ring can be removed using a flat bladed screwdriver. The machine shown is a Fagor.

Chapter 35

Buying spare parts

The aim of this manual has been to assist in the D.I.Y. repair of both your automatic combined washerdrier or tumble dry only machine. I hope that now, you will not only have a greater knowledge of how these machines work, but also the knowledge to prevent faults.

Above all, I hope that, armed with this information, you will feel confident enough to tackle most (if not all) of the faults that may arise with your machine from time to time.

However, all this knowledge and new found confidence could be wasted if you are unable to locate the spare parts needed to carry out the repair. In the past this would have been a problem, but in recent years the availability of spares have increased for several reasons:
1. The reluctance of people to pay high call out and labour charges for jobs that they feel they can do themselves.
2. The general interest in household D.I.Y. coupled with the saving from call out and labour charges, gives a feeling of satisfaction when the job is successfully completed.
3. The growth in size and number of D.I.Y. stores in recent years.
4. The improvement in the availability of pre-packed spares.

Many independent domestic appliance companies have been reluctant to supply parts for the D.I.Y. market in the past, but the current trend is to expand the amount of pre-packed spares. This has been confirmed by the three biggest independent spares suppliers of genuine and non-genuine (patterned) spares. The range of 'off the shelf' spare parts in both retail outlets and mail order companies is most welcome, and many machine manufacturers who do not have local dealerships will supply parts by post if requested. (Unfortunately this can sometimes be a lengthy process).

One way of obtaining the parts you require is to find a local 'spares and repairs' dealer through the yellow pages or local press. This is best done before your machine faults as you will then not waste time when a fault arises. In many instances you may possess more knowledge of your machine than the assistant in the shop, so it is essential to take the MAKE, MODEL and SERIAL NUMBER of your machine with you to help them locate or order the correct spare part for your requirements.

You may also find it quite helpful to take the faulty part(s) with you if possible, to confirm visually that it is the correct replacement. For instance, most pumps will look the same from memory, although quite substantial differences may be seen if the faulty item is compared with the newly offered item. The casing or mounting plate, etc., may be different. It is most annoying to get home only to find that two extra bolts are required.

PATTERNED PARTS

Certain parts that are widely available are marked 'suitable for' or 'to fit'. These are generally called patterned, or patent parts. Such terms refer to items or parts that are not supplied by the manufacturer of your machine, but are designed to fit it.

Some are copies of genuine parts and others are supplied by the original parts manufacturer to an independent distributor which are then supplied to the retailer and sold to the customer. This avoids the original manufacturer's markup as it is not an official or genuine spare part. This saving is then passed onto the customer.

Many of the appliance manufacturers disliked this procedure in the past, as the parts were of an inferior quality, but this is not the case today as the supply of parts is very big business and quality has improved dramatically. Although great savings can be made, care must be taken not to save money by buying inferior spare parts. Check the quality of the item first wherever possible. A reputable dealer should supply only good quality patterned or genuine parts.

Many of the original machine manufacturers are now discounting their genuine authorised spares to combat the growth in patterned spares. This is very good, as it can only benefit you, the customer.

GENUINE PARTS

Parts supplied by the manufacturer of your machine or

by their authorised local agent, are classed as 'genuine' and will in many cases, carry the companies trade mark or colours, etc., on the packaging. Many of the parts in todays machines are in fact not produced by the manufacturer of the finished machine, but a sub-contractor who also may supply a distributor of patterned spares with identical items.

Patterned spares producers will only take on items that have volume sales and leave the slow moving items to the original manufacturer of the machine. Generally it is a long procedure to obtain spares 'direct' from the manufacturer as many are unwilling to supply small orders direct to the public. Another system used to deter small orders is to use a 'pro-forma' invoicing sheet that will delay the receipt of parts until your cheque has cleared.

With the increase in D.I.Y., manufacturers are slowly changing their view regarding spares supply. This is simply to fend off the patterned spares, by making the original parts more available and competitively priced. Again this will in turn benefit the consumer.

PARTS BY POST

A free parts list of both patterned and genuine spares for most leading makes of machine can be obtained by writing to:

Dixon Repair Services
(Postal spares department)
Cranswick
Driffield
North Humberside
YO25 9QJ

Please enclose a large stamped addressed envelope and the make and model number of the relevant machine(s).

Parts can be obtained by post at competitive prices and payment can be made by cheque, Access or Visa.

IN CONCLUSION

Finally, the decision between genuine and patterned spares is yours, cost and speed of availability may have to be taken into consideration, but do not forsake quality for a small financial saving

As a guide we have compiled a list of manufacturers' names and addresses where parts may be obtained. Addresses other than these can be found in your local Yellow Pages.

Make	Telephone No.
AEG	0753 872325
Ariston	0322 526933
	(or see Yellow Pages under Merloni Domestic Appliances
Asko (was Asea)	081 568 4666
Bauknecht	0345 898989
Bendix	Yellow Pages
Bosch	081 573 6789
Candy	051 334 2781
Colston	see Ariston (above)
Creda	Yellow Pages
Electra	see Local Electricity Board
Electrolux	0325 300660
Fagor	0707 377877
Frigidaire	051 355 0588
Hotpoint	Local Directory
Hoover	Yellow Pages
Indesit	0322 526933
	(or see Yellow Pages under Merloni Domestic Appliances)
Kelvinator	051 334 2781
Miele	Yellow Pages
Philco	081 902 9626
Philips	
(now Whirlpool)	0345 898989
Servis	021 526 3199
Whirlpool	
(was Philips)	0345 898989
Zanussi	Yellow Pages/ Local Directory
Zerowatt	051 334 2781

Note: This information was correct at the time of publication, but may change with the course of time.

FURTHER INFORMATION

A detailed practial and instructional 55 minute video which complements the information relating to washing machines given in this publication is also available. For further details please write to the address at the bottom left of this page.

Chapter 36

Know your machine

This information is a guide only and the spaces represent the space left when the clothes are loaded normally. Do not compress the load to achieve the recommended amount of vacant space.

Most of us, you'll agree, would be completely lost without the range of gadgets we've become accustomed to using every day. Learning to take advantage of these time saving appliances, particularly your combined washerdrier or tumbledrier, will give you the freedom to look after yourself and your family in more important ways.

With our special needs in mind, washing machine manufacturers have developed the combined washerdrier and tumble dry only machines to help in both washing and drying our clothes.

Used properly, both types of machines can provide a thorough method of washing and drying. The special wash action of the front loading combined machines with their horizontal rotating drum mechanism creates sufficient agitation to effectively remove all dirt particles and even stubborn stains. However, it is important to use the correct types of washing powders/liquids in these machines. The low suds washing powder recommended by many major machine manufactures is Persil Automatic. The free movement given by the controlled lather level allows the clothes to be washer thoroughly and efficiently to give perfect results across all machine programmes, from a cotton boil was to a cool programme for silk and woollens. Automatic machines will also ensure that sufficient rinses are made to remove the dirty wash solution leaving your clothes completely clean, fresh and cared for.

Overloading your machine will greatly reduce cleaning efficiency, as the free movement of the clothes will be restricted. Your machine has a maximum load capacity which should not be exceeded.

This handy table will help you check your dry weight loads and was compiled with the help of Lever Bros.

Rule of thumb

To help in assessing the correct wash load, the drawing illustrates the maximum dry load size per selected programme.
A. Woollen and other fine fabrics requiring gentle washing – only a quarter of the drum should be occupied.
B. Synthetic and man made fibres requiring delicate washing – only half the drum space should be occupied.
C. Cottons and robust fabrics requiring higher temperatures and normal wash action – can occupy a greater proportion of the drum, leaving approximately a hand's width space at the top.

A.

B.

C.

Clothes

Blouse	cotton		150g	(5oz)
	other		100g	(3^1/2oz)
Dress	cotton		500g	(1lb 2oz)
	other		350g	(12oz)
Dressing Gown			700g	(1lb 8oz)
Jeans			700g	(1lb 8oz)
10 Nappies			1000g	(2lb 3oz)
Nightdress			150g	(5oz)
Pyjamas	cotton		350g	(12oz)
Shirt	cotton		300g	(10oz)
	other		200g	(7oz)
Skirt			200g	(7oz)
Suit, bulked polyester			1500g	(3lb 5oz)
Sweater	wool		400g	(14oz)
	other heavy		350g	(12oz)
	lightweight		200g	(7oz)
Tracksuit			1000g	(2lb 3oz)
Teeshirt			125g	(4^1/2oz)
Vest			125g	(4^1/2oz)

Household items

Bedspread	candlewick	(D)	3000g	(6lb 10oz)
		(S)	2000g	(4lb 6oz)
Blanket	wool	(D)	2000g	(4lb 6oz)
		(S)	1500g	(3lb 5oz)
	acrylic	(D)	1500g	(3lb 5oz)
		(S)	1000g	(2lb 3oz)
Cot Sheet			200g	(7oz)
Duvet Cover	cotton	(D)	1500g	(3lb 5oz)
	other	(D)	1000g	(2lb 3oz)
Pillow			900g	(2lb)
Pillowslip			125g	(4^1/2oz)
Tablecloth	large		700g	(1lb 8oz)
	small		250g	(9oz)
Tea Towels			100g	(3^1/2oz)
Towel	bath		700g	(1lb 8oz)
	hand		250g	(9oz)
Sheet	cotton	(D)	1000g	(2lb 3oz)
		(S)	750g	(1lb 10oz)
	other	(D)	500g	(1lb 2oz)
		(S)	350g	(12oz)

Chapter 37

Common causes of poor washing results

Poor washing is more often than not due to the incorrect operation of the machine by the user, rather than a mechanical or electrical fault of the machine. The most common user faults are listed below.

1. Mis-use of the controls
(a) To achieve good consistent results for your washing, you must have a thorough understanding of your machine and its controls. Always remember, you tell the machine what to do. If in doubt, read the manufacturer's manual.
(b) Does the selected programme have the right water temperature and wash time for the fabrics in the load?

2. Incorrect dosage
(a) The amount of powder/liquid that you should use is usually displayed on the side of the pack. Please remember that this is only a guide, and the amounts have to be adjusted to load size, type and degree of soiling, and the 'hardness' of the water supply.
(b) Is the container that is used for measuring the powder/liquid accurate? On the large sized packs one measure of powder should weigh 3 oz. With the recent advent of 'compact' powders, use the scoop provided and remember that one scoop is normally equal to 1 cup of the previous bulkier powders.
(c) Have you made allowances for special types of soiling? Ointments, thick creams, heavy perspiration and similar, use up the suds activity very quickly. This can be compensated for by adding an extra half cupful (or scoop) of powder.
Note: Poor degree of soil and stain removal, the greying of whites or the appearance of 'greasy balls' on the washed clothes is a clear indication of under-dosing. It is never through over-dosing.

3. Water supply
Washing powder is formulated to do several tasks:
(a) Overcome water hardness.
(b) Wet-out the fabrics.
(c) Remove the soiling from the clothes.
(d) Hold the soiling in suspension, away from the clothes.

It is obvious that the harder the water the harder the detergent has to work. More detergent should be added in the case of hard water and less in the case of soft water. The local area water authority should be able to advise you on the hardness of the water in your area.

4. Incorrect loading
(a) Overloading the washer will result in the clothes not being able to move freely inside the drum, resulting in inadequate soil removal
(b) Some programmes require reduced loads. If one of these programmes is used, then reduce the load. If you are not sure, read the manufacturer's manual.

5. Other factors
(a) How old is the machine? Like any appliance, a washing machine has a restricted lifespan. In the case of an automatic washing machine, the average lifespan is around eight years (manufacturer's figures).
(b) When was the machine last serviced? (c) Poor whiteness is a result of constant under-dosing and mixed loads. With the soiling not being removed, there is a gradual build up of deposits in the clothes. This can be avoided by using the correct dosage and loading with like fabrics, i.e. all whites.
(d) Domestic changes can reflect the quality of the wash, i.e. have you moved area? see 3. Is there a new addition to the family? see 2c.
(e) Are the poor results evident on all programmes or only on specific programmes? see 4.
(f) Most of the manufacturers recommend an idle wash to keep the machine clean and free from deposits. This means a wash with no powder or clothes every month or so.
(g) Have you read the manufacturer's manual? Improvements on poor colours and whites will not happen magically, the process is very

gradual. Once a good whiteness has been achieved, correct washing and dosing is the only way to maintain the standard.

Six golden rules for best results
1. Wash clothes frequently. Modern fabrics, particularly the man-made fibres, need frequent washing or dirt may become absorbed into the fibres.
2. Use the right amount of detergent. Refer to the side of the packet for the correct dosage.
3. Choose the recommended wash code and machine programme for the fabric. To safeguard colour and finish, preserve shape and minimise creasing, never wash hotter, wash longer or spin longer than is indicated by the correct wash code for the fabric.
4. Thorough rinsing is essential. Some finishes such as shower-proofing lose their effectiveness if not well rinsed, towelling fabrics particularly nappies, may become harsh and scratchy. Always rinse at least twice.
5. Treat stains quickly. Give first-aid treatment immediately whenever possible, by blotting with an absorbent tissue. Never neglect a stain and never rub, this may push it further into the fabric. Pinch out as much as you can.
6. Dry 'easy care' fabrics correctly. Check the instructions on the label. Easy care fabrics of cotton or man-made fibre should be rinsed in cold water and should be put in the spinner for only a few seconds. DO NOT forget to check pockets for coins and tissues, etc., and fasten all zippers.

Chapter 38

Successful stain removal

Stains on washable fabrics fall into two groups:

GROUP ONE – STAINS THAT WILL WASH OUT IN SOAP OR DETERGENT SUDS

Type of stain

Beetroot, Blood, Blackcurrent and other fruit juices, Chocolate, Cream, Cocoa, Coffee, Egg, Gravy, Ice lollies, Jam, Meat juice, Mud, Milk, Nappy stains, Pickles, Soft drinks, Sauces, Soup, Stews, Syrup, Tea, Tomato ketchup, Wines and Spirits and Washable ink.

Method

Fresh stains – Soak in cold suds to keep the stain from becoming set in fabric. Then wash in the normal way according to the fabric.

Old dried-in stains – Lubricate with glycerine. Apply a mixture of one part glycerine to two parts water to the stain and leave for 10 minutes. Then treat as fresh stains.

Residual marks – *White fabrics only*. Bleach out with Hydrogen Peroxide solution. (One part 20 volume hydrogen peroxide to nine parts water). Leave soaking in this solution for 1 hour. Then wash in the normal way. Blood stains may leave residual iron mould marks, which should be

treated as for iron mould.
Special Note: For 'built' stains such as egg (cooked), chocolate and mud, scrape off surplus staining matter first before putting to soak. Blood and meat juice stains whether fresh or old should be soaked in cold water first.

GROUP TWO – 'TREAT-'N-WASH' STAINS

What you will need

Glycerine (for lubrication)
Methylated Spirit (handle carefully: *Inflammable Poisonous)*.
Turpentine *(Inflammable)*.
Amyl Acetate (handle carefully – *Highly inflammable*).
Hydrogen peroxide.
Proprietary grease solvent – 'Thawpit', 'Beaucare', 'Dab- it-off', etc., (*Do not breathe the vapour: Use in a well ventilated room*).
Photographic Hypo.
White vinegar (acetic acid).
Household ammonia (keep away from eyes).
Cotton wool, Paper tissues, etc

HANDY HINTS

1. Act quickly to remove a stain and prevent it ' setting'. The faster you act, the milder the remedy needed.
2. Never rub a stain, as this pushes it further into the fabric.

'Pinch out' as much as you can, using a clean cloth or a paper tissue.
3. Never neglect a stain. The more drastic remedies for 'set' stains may harm delicate fabrics. If some stains are left on man-made and drip-dry fabrics in particular, they can be absorbed permanently into the fabric itself. Stains such as iron mould (rust) can weaken cellulosic fabrics and may eventually cause holes.
4. When applying solvents, always work from outside the stain towards the centre to avoid making a ring.
5. Always try a solvent on a hidden part first (e.g. under hem or seam allowance) to make sure it does not harm colours or fabric.
6. Stains on garments to be 'dry-cleaned' should be indicated on the garment (e.g. with a coloured tacking thread). Tell the cleaners what has caused the stain. This facilitates the task of removal and lessens the risk of the stain becoming permanently set by incorrect treatment.

ABSORBENT PAD METHOD

Using two absorbent pads of cotton wool, one soaked with the solvent and other held against the stain. Dab the underside of the stain with solvent and the staining matter will be transferred from the material to the top pad. Change this pad around to a clean part and continue working in this way until no more staining matter comes through. To remove last traces of the stain, wash in usual way.

Type of stain	Solvent	Method
Ballpoint ink	Methylated spirit (INF) (Benzine for acetate and 'Tricel')	Absorbent pad method
Bicycle oil	Proprietary grease solvent	Absorbent pad method or follow manufacturer's instructions
Black lead	Proprietary grease solvent	Absorbent pad method or follow manufacturer's instructions
Chalks and Crayons (Washable)		Brush off as much as possible while dry. Then brush stained area with suds (one dessertspoonful to a pint of water). Wash in the usual way.
Chalks and Crayons (Indelible)	Methylated spirit. (INF) (Benzine for acetate and 'Tricel'). (INF)	Absorbent pad method
Chewing gum	Methylated spirit. (INF) (Benzine for acetate and 'Tricel'). (INF)	Absorbent pad method Alternatively rub the gum with an ice cube to harden it. It may then be picked off by hand. Wash as usual to remove final traces.
Cod Liver Oil, Cooking Fat, Heavy grease stains	Proprietary grease solvent	Absorbent pad method or manufacturer's instructions
Contact adhesives. (e.g. Balsa cement, 'Evostick')	Amyl Acetate. (INF)	Absorbent pad method.
Felt pen inks	Methylated spirit. (INF) (Benzine for acetate and 'Tricel'). (INF)	First, lubricate the stain by rubbing with hard soap, and then wash in the usual way. For obstinate stains, use Methylated Spirit and absorbent pad method. Wash again to remove final traces.
Grass	Methylated spirit. (INF) (Benzine for acetate and 'Tricel'). (INF)	Absorbent pad method

Type of stain	Solvent	Method
Greasepaint	Proprietary grease solvent	Absorbent pad method or follow manufacturer's instructions
Hair lacquer	Amyl Acetate, (INF)	Absorbent pad method
Iodine	Photographic Hypo	Dissolve one tablespoon hypo crystals in one pint warm water. Soak the stain for about 5 minutes, watching closely. As soon as the stain disappears, rinse thoroughly, then wash in the usual way.
Iron mould (rust marks)	a) Lemon juice (for wool, man-made fibres and all fine fabrics)	Apply lemon juice to the stain and leave it for 10-15 minutes. Place a damp cloth over the stain and iron. Repeat several times, as necessary. Rinse and wash as usual.
	b) Oxalic acid solution (for white cotton and linen only) use with care	Dissolve $\frac{1}{2}$ teaspoonful oxalic acid crystals in $\frac{1}{2}$ pint hot water. Tie a piece of cotton tightly round the stained area (to prevent the solution spreading) and immerse the stained part only. Leave for 2 or 3 minutes. Rinse thoroughly and wash in rich suds.
Lipstick and Rouge i) light stains ii) heavy stains	Proprietary grease solvent	Soak then wash in usual way. Absorbent pad method or follow manufacturer's instructions
Marking ink	Marking ink eradicator (from stationers).	Follow instructions on the bottle label carefully.
Metal polish	Proprietary grease solvent	Absorbent pad method is regular soaking, followed manufacturer's instructions.

Successful stain removal

Type of stain	Solvent	Method
Mildew (mould on articles stored damp) a) coloured articles		The only treatment is regular soaking, followed by washing in rich suds – this will gradually reduce the marks.
b) white cottons and linens without special finishes	Household bleach and vinegar	Soak in one part bleach to 100 parts water with one tablespoonful vinegar. Rinse thoroughly, then wash.
c) white, drip-dry fabrics.	Hydrogen peroxide solution	Soak in one part hydrogen peroxide (20 volume) and nine parts water until staining has cleared. Rinse thoroughly then wash in the usual way.
Nail varnish	Amyl Acetate for all fabrics (INF)	Absorbent pad method
Nicotine (Tobacco juice)	Methylated spirit. (INF) (Benzine for acetate or 'Tricel'). (INF)	Absorbent pad method
Non-washable ink	Oxalic acid solution. (For white cottons and linens only).	See method (b) under iron mould
Paint: Emulsion	Water	Emulsion paint splashes sponged immediately with cold water will quickly be removed. Dried stains are permanent.
Paint: Oil	Turpentine or Amyl Acetate. (INF)	Absorbent pad method
Perspiration: Fresh stains	Ammonia. **Do not inhale the fumes**.	Damp with water, then hold over an open bottle of household ammonia
Perspiration: Old stains	White vinegar	Sponge with white vinegar, rinse thoroughly, then wash in usual way

Type of stain	Solvent	Method
'Plasticine' Modelling clay	Proprietary grease solvent or lighter fuel. (INF)	Scrape or brush off as much as possible. Apply solvent with absorbent pad method – wash to remove final traces.
Scorch: a) Light marks		Light stains will sometimes respond to treatment as for Group 1 – washable stains.
	Glycerine	If persistent, moisten with water and rub glycerine into the stained area. Wash through. Residual marks may respond to soaking in hydrogen peroxide solution.
b) Heavy marks	Heavy scorch marks that have damaged the fibres cannot be removed	
Shoe polish	Glycerine and proprietary grease solvent	Lubricate stain with glycerine, then use solvent with absorbent pad method or follow manufacturer's instructions. Wash to remove final traces.
Sun tan oil	Proprietary grease solvent	Absorbent pad method or follow manufacturer's instructions
Tar	Eucalyptus oil, Proprietary grease solvent, Benzine or lighter fuel, (INF)	Scrape off surplus, then apply solvent with absorbent pad method. Rinse and wash as soon as possible.
Verdigris (green stains from copper pipes, etc.)		Treat as iron mould

Special Note: Cotton garments with flame- resistant finishes must **not** be treated with household (chlorine) bleach or hydrogen peroxide in stain removal treatment, since this may impair the finish.

Keep solvents securely closed, labelled and out of children's reach.

Chapter 39

Care labelling in the UK

OTHER SYMBOLS WITHIN THE INTERNATIONAL SYSTEM

 A triangle is the symbol used to indicate the bleach may be used.

 Sometimes the triangle contains the letters 'Cl' which stands for chlorine. It therefore means a household (chlorine) bleach such as 'Domestos'.

 If the symbol is crossed out, this means that household (chlorine) bleach must **not** be used. If this instruction is ignored the fabric/finish/dye could be seriously affected.

DRY CLEANING

◯ A circle is the symbol used for dry-cleaning instructions. It will never appear on its own but will have additional information as follows:

Ⓐ Articles normal for dry-cleaning in all solvents.

Ⓟ Articles normal for dry-cleaning in perchloro-ethylene, white spirit, Solvent 113 and Solvent 11.

Ⓕ Articles normal for dry-cleaning in white spirit or Solvent 113.

⊗ Do **not** dry-clean.

To help housewives all over the country to know what washing conditions should be followed, the Home Laundering Consultative Council was formed from representatives of washing powder and washing machine manufacturers and the textile trade. The Council determined eight washing processes known as the British Textile Care Labelling Scheme and although this scheme has been superseded by a later more universal system, garment labels and washing machine controls and instructions produced under the eight British Codes will still be in evidence.

As from January 1974, a new system, the result of negotiations between the Home Laundering Consultative Council and the International Care Labelling Symposium, came into being. This is known as **The International Textile Care Labelling Code**.

WHAT THE SYMBOLS MEAN

The wash tub symbol indicates a particular washing process most appropriate to a fabric or group of fabrics. It recommends:
The maximum safe washing temperature.
The amount of agitation during the wash.
The method of water extraction

AGITATION TIMES

Maximum wash – means the longest agitation time for any machine as defined by the machine manufacturers.
Medium wash – is 40–60% of the maximum time.
Minimum wash – is 20–30% of the maximum time.
Hand wash – apply the label instructions as to the vigour of the wash to the particular circumstances. For fabric groups 6, 7 and 8 do not rub – squeeze the suds gently through the garment.

WATER EXTRACTION

Instructions for this are in the main self-explanatory. It advises whether:
A cold rinse before spinning would be beneficial;
A long or short spin or no spinning or wringing is needed.
Note – Short Spin is the minimum spinning time as defined by the manufacturers for their appliance – e.g. 15 seconds only for man-made fibre fabrics, to avoid creasing.
When in doubt, spin-dry for the time necessary to remove surplus moisture only.

IRONING

 This symbol is used to provide ironing instructions. The number of dots within the symbol is varied to indicate the correct temperature setting, as follows:

 One dot = cool.

 Two dots = warm.

 Three dots = hot.

 Crossed out = **do not iron**.

DRYING

 The vast majority of textile articles can safely be tumble dried. Care labels may be used to indicate either that tumble drying is the optimum drying method for a particular article, or that tumble drying should not be used if the article is likely to be harmed by this treatment.

 Tumble drying beneficial.

Do **not** tumble dry.

In cases where the tumble drying prohibition symbol is used, any special positive instructions, such as 'dry flat' for heavier weight knitwear, should be given in words.

EXPLANATION OF DRYING SYMBOLS USED BY OTHER COUNTRIES

 Articles can be tumble-dried.

 Drip drying is recommended.

 Hang = line-dry.

 Dry flat.

MIXED FABRIC GROUP LOADS

Ideally fabric groups should not be mixed to make up a wash-load. Unless care is taken it does increase the risk of shrinkage, or dye contamination and discoloration of white things (particularly nylon) from articles which prove non-colourfast under the wash conditions. However, if for convenience or for the sake of economy, there is no alternative, always select the mildest wash conditions and use the following table as a guide:

Fabric codes 1 and 2 together – wash as code 2.
Fabric codes 3 and 4 together – wash as code 4.
Fabric codes 6 and 7 together – wash as code 6.
However, woollen garments must not be rubbed or hand wrung, as this could distort the fibre. White nylon or articles from codes 5 and 8 should always be washed alone.

FABRIC CONDITIONING

No matter how thoroughly clothes are rinsed, after repeated washing and rinsing they gradually lose their bulk and softness. Fabric conditioner in the final rinse untangles matted fibres restoring the natural bulk and bounce to the fabric. But fabric conditioner is not only about softness on towels and woollens, it is about care for all your wash

SPECIAL NOTE ON VELVET

Velvet is a construction term, not a fibre. It may be silk, cotton or an acetate/nylon blend, e.g., 'Tricelon'. For best results look for the wash-care label and follow the instructions faithfully. If in doubt, dry-clean.

Soft furnishings in velvet weave, e.g., dralon – it is helpful to remove surface dust with a vacuum cleaner or soft brush. 'Dralon' velvet is not washable. It can be cleaned with a dry-foam shampoo. Avoid saturating cotton backing, vacuum or brush foam off when dry. When dry-cleaning state fibre content.

FLAME-RETARDANT FABRICS AND FINISHES

Apart from nylon and wool, which are regarded as being of low flammability, there are two ways of giving fabrics flame-retardant properties:
(a) by the application to cotton fabrics of a special finish such as 'Proban', 'Pyrovatex', 'Timonox'. Also in certain cases to wool, though this as yet is not being widely used for apparel purposes.
(b) by the modification of the fibre itself, e.g., fibres like acrylic but with modified properties. The generic term for these is modacrylic, e.g., 'Teklan' or Monsanto's modacrylic. They are inherently flame retardant.

The appropriate washing codes are:

4/50	Cotton
7/40	Wool
6/40	Modacrylics

IMPORTANT

Flame-retardant fabrics, e.g., modacrylics or fabrics with a flame-retardant finish must not be bleached, or soaked in any washing product.

Fabrics with a flame-retardant finish must not be washed in soap or non-automatic powder as soap can mask the properties of the finish. Other types of washing product, including automatic powder may be used with safety. Rinse very thoroughly.

HAND CARE

To get the best results in the hand wash make sure the detergent is thoroughly dissolved before washing and the clothes thoroughly rinsed afterwards.

After each wash by hand, rinse your hands and dry them thoroughly. People with sensitive or damaged skin should pay particular attention to the instructions for use and avoid prolonged contact.

'SPECIAL FINISH' LABELS

e.g. 'machine washable wool' – Sometimes the finish given to a fabric changes its washability. Where there is no wash-care guidance provided, check the name of the finish to see whether there are any special care instructions.

NO LABEL PROVIDED

If in doubt wash under the mildest conditions, i.e., use warm 40°C suds only; do not soak; wash through quickly and gently; rinse thoroughly; blot off surplus moisture with a towel and dry carefully. If washing by machine choose the gentlest programme. If ironing seems appropriate, use a cool iron.

WASH FOR THE FABRIC, NEVER MIND THE SHAPE!

Remember always that it is the fabric and its construction rather than the type of article that decides the washing treatment. A polyester shirt will be grouped with a textured polyester suit, a small boy's polyester/'Viloft' trousers and his sister's polyester blouse. They are all different shapes and sizes but all will be washed as polyester requires, in hand-hot suds with cold rinsing and a short spin.

Different fabrics require different washing temperatures and agitation times. So ignore the *shape* of the article and concern yourself only with what it is made of and then wash it according to the appropriate Care Labelling Code.

SPECIAL GUIDANCE

Blends and mixtures

A *blend fabric* is one which has been woven or knitted from yarn made by the blending of two or more fibres, prior to the yarn being spun. A *mixture fabric* is one where two or more different yarns are used during weaving or knitting (e.g., a nylon warp woven into a viscose or cotton weft). In both cases the fibre which needs the milder treatment influences the wash conditions suitable for the fabric. For example a polyester/wool blend should only be washed in warm suds, because of the wool content; polyester/cotton and acrylic/cotton are both washed at temperatures lower than the maximum for cotton. If in doubt, wash as for the fibre requiring the milder treatment.

Colour fastness

Test for colour fastness by damping a piece of the hem or seam allowance and iron a piece of dry white fabric on to it. If any colour blots off, wash the article separately, in very cool suds, and rinse at once in cold water. Put to dry immediately. If the colour is very loose, dry cleaning may be advisable (check the label).

SOAKING

There are occasions when heavily soiled or stained articles benefit from a soak before washing, particularly those included in fabric group code 1. Before soaking any coloured article it is important to make sure that:

The dye is fast to soaking – if in doubt do not soak;

The washing powder is completely dissolved before putting in the articles;

The water temperature is not too high for the fabric or the dye;

The article is not **bunched up** – it should be left as free as possible;

White and coloured articles are not soaked together – this is especially necessary where white nylon is concerned as nylon stockings and tights, for example, are seldom fast to soaking for long periods;

The articles do not have metal buttons or metal fasteners – soaking can encourage iron mould (brown stains).

Articles made from wool or silk or from fabric with a flame-retardant finish, whether white or coloured, should *never be soaked in washing products of any type*.

Changes in wash coding – October 1987

From October 1987 a change in the clothes labelling was introduced. Shown here is a comparison chart between old and new styles. This should help in the transition period when you will have garments bearing both types of labelling. The idea is to give more information on the garment itself, to aid washing and whether or not to mix loads, etc. In the long run, such information will be most helpful and I believe welcomed by all.

OLD	NEW	Examples of Application
1 / 95°	95	White cotton and linen articles without special finishes
2 / 60°	60	Cotton, linen or viscose articles without special finishes where colours are fast at 60°C
3 / 60°	60	(Not used in UK) White nylon and white polyester/cotton mixtures are included in [50]
4 / 50°	50	Nylon; polyester/cotton mixtures; polyester cotton and viscose articles with special finishes; cotton/acrylic mixtures
5 / 40°	40	Cotton, linen or viscose articles, where colours are fast at 40°C but not at 60°C
6 / 40°	40	Acrylics, acetate and triacetate, including mixtures with wool; polyester/wool blends
7 / 40°	40	Wool, wool mixed with other fibres; silk
8 / 30°	30	*(Not used in UK) See items included in [40] and [40]
9 / 95°	95	(Not applicable in UK)
handwash	handwash	Handwash (Do not machine wash)
do not wash	do not wash	Do not wash

* For this process in other countries the single ▬ means much reduced machine action.

MIXING WASH LOADS

As a general guide you can mix wash labels without a bar provided you wash at the lowest temperature shown.

e.g. ⌊60⌋ and ⌊40⌋ can be washed together at 40°C.

Likewise, you can mix wash labels with and without a bar provided that, again, you wash at the lowest temperature, BUT you must also reduce the washing action.

e.g. ⌊60⌋ and ⌊40⌋ can be washed together at 40°C at a reduced action.

Articles with ⌊40⌋ must be washed as wool at a much reduced action.

REMEMBER "wash separately" means what it says.

EXAMPLES OF THE NEW LABEL FORMATS

⌊50⌋	MACHINE	HAND WASH
	Hand hot medium wash	Hand hot
Wash as Synthetics	Cold rinse. Short spin or drip-dry	
⊠	DO NOT USE CHLORINE BLEACH	
◯	MAY BE TUMBLE DRIED	
🏷️	WARM	
Ⓟ	DRY CLEANABLE	

⌊50⌋	MACHINE OR HAND WASH	Ⓟ Dry Cleanable
⊠ Do not Bleach	◯ Tumble Dry	🏷️ Cool Iron

	MACHINE	HAND WASH
⌊50⌋	Hand hot medium wash	Hand hot
	Cold rinse. Short spin or drip-dry	
	Wash as Synthetics	
⊠ DO NOT USE CHLORINE BLEACH	◯ MAY BE TUMBLE DRIED	🏷️ WARM IRON / Ⓟ DRY CLEAN ABLE

Chapter 40
Jargon

Amp – Short for ampere. Used to measure the flow of electricity through a circuit or appliance.

Armature – Wire wound centre of brush motor.

Bi-metal – Two different metals which have been joined together. When heated the strip bends in a known direction.

Boss – Protection around entry point.

Burn-out – Overheated part of item.

Bus bar – An electrical conductor.

Cable – Conductors covered with a protective semi-rigid insulating sheath, used to connect the individual components within a wiring system.

Carbon face (seal) – Watertight flat surface seal.

Centrifugal – Force that increases with rotation causing movement away from its centre.

Circuit – Any complete path for an electric current, allowing it to pass along a 'live' conductor to where it is needed and then to return to its source along a 'neutral' conductor.

Clamp band – Large adjustable clip used for holding door boot.

Closed circuit – A normal circuit that allows power to pass through.

Collet – Tapered sleeve of two or more parts designed to grip a shaft passed through its centre.

Commutator – Copper segment on motor armature.

Component – Individual parts of the machine, i.e. pump, valves, motors, are all components.

Conductor – The metallic current-carrying 'cores' within cable or flex.

Consumer Unit – Unit governing the supply of electricity to all circuits and containing a main on-off switch and fuses or circuit breakers protecting the circuits emanating from it.

Contact – Point at which switch makes contact.

Continuity – Electrical path with no break.

Corbin – Type of spring hose clip.

Damped – To have reduced movement of suspension, i.e. reduce oscillation of tub unit during distribute and spin cycles.

Dispenser – Compartment that holds detergent ready for use.

Dispenser hose – Hose that supplies the tub with detergent and water from the dispenser compartment.

Distribute – To balance load by centrifugal force, i.e. a set speed calculated to even out wash load prior to faster spin.

Door boot – Flexible seal between door and tub.

Door gasket –Flexible seal between door and tub.

Door seal – Flexible seal between door and tub.

Drift – Soft metal rod used for bearing removal.

E.L.C.B. – Earth leakage circuit breaker – see R.C.C.B.

E.M.F. – Source of energy that can cause a current to flow in a circuit or device.

Early – Machine not currently on the market.

Energize (Energise) – To supply power to.

Energized (Energised) – Having power supplied to.

Flowchart – Method of following complicated steps in a logical fashion.

Functional test – To test machine on a set programme.

Garter ring – Large elastic band or spring used to secure door boot.

Grommet fitting – Method of fitting hoses, etc., requiring no clips.

Harness – Electrical wiring within a machine.

Hertz – Periodic cycle of one second, i.e. cycles per second.

'Hunting' – Oscillating.

Impeller – The blades of the water pump.

Insulation – Material used to insulate a device or a region.

Isolate – To disconnect from the electricity supply and water supply etc.

Laminations – Joined metal parts of stator.

Late – Current machine on market.

Lint – Fluff from clothing that may cause a small blockage.

Live – Supply current carrying conductor.

Make – 1. Manufacturer's name.

2. When a switch makes contact it is said to make.

Micro-processor – Miniature integrated circuit containing programme information.

Miniature Circuit Breaker – (MCB) a device used instead of fuses to isolate a circuit if fault/overload occurs.

Neutral – Return current carrying conductor.

O.O.B. – Out of balance detection system.

Open-circuit – Circuit that is broken, i.e. will not let any power through.

Outer casing – Cabinet, 'shell' of the machine.

P.S.I. – Measurement of water pressure, pounds per square inch, e.g. 38 p.s.i.

Pawl – Pivoted lever designed to engage ratchet gearing.

Porous – Item that allows water to pass through.

Potentiometer – Variable resistance device.

Processor – Main central processing component of computer control circuitry.

Programmer – see Timer.

P.T.F.E. – Special lubricant (mainly for tumbledriers) chemical name – Polytetrafluorethylene

R.C.C.B. – Residual current circuit breaker (also known as R.C.D.)

R.C.D. – Residual current device. See also – E.L.C.B. and R.C.C.B.

Reciprocating – Mechanical action of backwards and forwards movement.

Reverse polarity – A situation where live and neutral feeds have reversed, e.g. connected incorrectly at supply, socket or plug.

Ribbon cable – Flat cable used for low voltage P.C.B. connections.

Rotor – Central part of an induction motor.

Schematic diagram – Theoretical diagram.

Seal – Piece of pre-shaped rubber that usually fits into a purpose built groove or between two surfaces, therefore creating a watertight seal when subjected to pressure.

Sealant – Rubber substance used for ensuring watertight joints.

Shell – Outer of machine.

Spades – Connections on wires or components – remove gently.

Stat – Abbreviation of thermostat.

Stator – Electrical winding on motor.

Terminal block – A method of connecting wires together safely.

T.O.C. – Thermal overload cut-out. At a pre-set temperature, the T.O.C. will break electrical current to whatever it is in circuit with, i.e. prevents motors, etc., overheating.

Thermistor – A semi-conductor device, the resistance of which is affected by temperatures.

Thermostat – Device used to monitor temperature.

Thyristor – Electronic switching device.

Triac – Electronic switching device.

Volt – Unit of electrical pressure (potential) difference. In most British homes the mains voltage is 240v.

Volatile (when relating to computer control applications) – Unable to store information when power is turned off.

Non-volatile (when relating to computer control applications) – Retains information for a set period even with power turned off.

Watt – Unit of power consumed by an appliance or circuit, the product of the mains voltage and the current drawn (in amps). 1000 W = 1 kilowatt (kw).